KENT DIALECT

A Selection of Words and Anecdotes from Around Kent

By

Ian Howe

BRADWELL
BOOKS

Published by Bradwell Books
9 Orgreave Close Sheffield S13 9NP
Email - books@bradwellbooks.co.uk
©Ian Howe 2012

British Library Cataloguing in Publication Data -
a catalogue record for this book is available from
the British Library.

1st Edition
ISBN - 9781902674346
Print - Gomer Press, Llandysul, Ceredigion SA44 4JL

Design by JenksDesign@yahoo.co.uk

INTRODUCTION

In a world of global communication and social networking the many dialects that are spoken around this island nation have come under increasing threat. English has always been in a process of flux. The invasion led by William the Conqueror in 1066, for example, brought in Norman French, which came to sit alongside – or often replace – the existing Anglo-Saxon. An astonishing variety of different dialects once existed, but developments in communication, from the printing press to the internet, have led to increasing standardisation of vocabulary and grammar.

The dialect of Kent, unlike many of its equivalents in other areas, has in fact had a considerable influence on modern standard English. When Caxton's printing press started the process of standardisation, the form of English that made up many of the earliest printed texts was that of London and the Home Counties, with the result that many old Kentish words are now familiar to all English speakers ('abide', 'ruck' etc.) while the pronunciation that was typical of Kent often became the standard form ('left' rather than 'lift', for example).

As a result of the influence of the Kentish tongue on modern English, with many words still familiar to us today, speakers of the local dialect are perhaps most noticeable through the use of certain turns of phrase, strange compound words and unusual pronunciations than radically different language. Many examples in the first two categories can be found in the lists in this book.

A

Act-about - to fool around, play the fool

Adle or **addle** - confused, dazed

Afore - before

Against - in time for when, by the time that

Agin - against, near

Airy - of weather, blustery or windy

Akers - acorns

All-on - continually

Allow - to think of, consider, regard

Allworks - a farm labourer available to take on any kind of work

Amonst the middlins - in reasonable health

Amper - a swelling or blemish

An - often used in place of 'of' or 'on'

Anents - opposite, over against

Anointed - troublesome, mischievous

Anthony-pig - the runt of the litter (supposedly protected by St Anthony)

Aquabob - icicle

Arber - elbow

Arbitry - greedy, grasping

Arkie - ear

Arrant - errand

Arrivance - birthplace, place of origin

Asprawl - awry, gone wrong

Awlin - a measure of length (c. 5ft 7ins) used to measure nets

Ax - to ask

B

Backening - a relapse; a hindrance

Backer - a porter or carrier (especially at a quay or dock)

Back-out, backside or **backway** - the back yard of a house or dwelling

Bain't - are not

Bait - food eaten by men at work in the fields

Bald - bold, brave

Ball squab - a newly hatched bird

Bannick or **bannock** - to hit or strike a person or animal

Barm - brewer's yeast

Barth - a shelter for cattle

Baully or **bawley** - a boat, specifically a small fishing smack

Beanfeast - a celebration

Beaver or **beevor** - a breakfast or morning meal taken by dockers or labourers

Because why? - why, for what reason?

Beetle - a wooden mallet

Before after - until

Bele - a boil

Beleft - believed

Below London - not in Kent (see also 'sheers')

Bender and arrs - bow and arrows

Besom - (1) a small broom (2) a mischievous child (3) a young woman of questionable character

Better-most or **bettermy** - best, superior

Bibber - to tremble

Bishop's finger - signpost

B

Black-tan - a good-for-nothing
Blar or **blare** - to bleat, low or bellow
Blether - to talk nonsense
Bligh - dull, lonely
Bloomage - plumage
Blouse - to sweat profusely, to be red-faced; a red-faced girl
Bly - likeness, resemblance
Bobbery - a squabble or falling-out
Boblight - twilight
Bodily-ill - suffering from a fever or illness rather than a physical injury
Boffle - to confuse; confusion
Borstal or **bostal** - a path up a steep hill
Bounds - in 'no bounds', expresses uncertainty, e.g. Of location
Boy-beat - outdone or beaten by someone younger than yourself
Brack - a crack or tear
Brave - big, large
Brenbutter - bread and butter
Brent - steep
Bret - to change, alter, fade away
Brown-deep - lost in thought
Bruff - blunt, rough or rude
Brumpt - broke or bankrupted
Bruss - proud, petulant, forward
Buck - a pile of laundry; to wash
Buggy - easily upset or irritated
Bumblesome - clumsy, awkward, ill-fitting

C

Cailes - skittles, ninepins
Call-over - to find fault with, abuse, reprimand
Cantel - an indefinite number or amount
Car - to carry
Carpet-way - a smooth grass road
Carvet - (1) a thick hedgerow (2) a piece of land carved out of another
Cast - (1) defeated, beaten (2) the pile of soil produced by a mole, ant or worm
Ceremony - fuss, palaver
Chald - cold
Charnail or **charnel** - a hinge
Chart - area of rough common ground
Chatsome - talkative
Chavish - peevish, fretful
Cheaste - strife
Cheese-bug - woodlouse
Chiese - to choose
Chitter - wren
Christ-cross - the alphabet
Clean - entirely, completely
Cledge - stiff clay
Clever - in good health
Clinkers - the cinders left behind in a fire or furnace
Cluck - unwell, lacking in strength
Cluther - (1) a great deal of noise (2) to make a lot of noise
Cobble, cock-bell or cogbell - an icicle
Cocker - to spoil or indulge (a child)
Composant - St Elmo's Fire, a glowing light around the mast of a ship

C

Conniver - to gape or stare
Copse - a fence across a dyke, with no opening
Cotchering - gossiping
Cotton - to be in agreement with one another
Coved or **coven** - with sloping sides
Coverlid or **covertlid** - the outer covering on a bed
Cow - (1) a pitcher (2) the moveable top, or cowl, of an oast house
Cramp-word - an obscure or difficult word
Crips - crisp
Crow-fish - stickleback
Cruppish - peevish, out of sorts
Culch - rubbish, litter or any sort of refuse

D

Dabberry - gooseberry
Daffy - a large quantity or number of something
Dappy - half-witted
Dawther or **dodder** - to shake or tremble; to move as if infirm
Dawthery - feeble, trembling, shaky
Dead-alive - dull, stupid
Deathness - deafness
Dee - day
Deek - a ditch or dyke
Den or **dene** - a wooded valley
Denial - a hindrance or drawback
Destiny - destination
Dewlaps - overstockings of coarse wool

D

Dick - a dyke or ditch
Dicky - ill, out of sorts, poorly
Didos - tricks, pranks
Disguised - tipsy, slightly drunk
Dissight - a blemish or defect
Doated or **doited** - rotten, decayed
Dobbin - temper
Dole - a boundary stone
Dollymosh - to destroy, demolish or spoil completely
Dolphin - a fly or aphid that blights roses and other plants
Dorick - frolic, lark or spree
Doztren - daughters
Drean - to drip
Dreckly-minute - immediately, at once (from 'directly this minute')
Drill - to waste away gradually
Dryth - thirst, drought
Dumbledore - bumble bee
Dunty - stupid, confused
Dwindle - a poor, sickly child

E

Ecker - to stammer or stutter
Edder - adder
Effet - newt
Ellinge - solitary, lonely
Emmet - ant
Emmet cast - anthill

E

Entetig - to introduce
Ersh - stubble that remains after the corn has been cut

F

Fader - father
Fakement - pain, discomfort, distress
Fanteg or **fanteeg** - state of excitement, worry or passion
Fantod - nervous, fidgety, restless
Fargo or **fogo** - a stink, stench or bad smell
Fease - (1) to fret or worry (2) a fretful child
Feetens - footprints
Fellowly - familiar, companionable, free
Fenny - dirty, mouldy
Fickle - to put an idea into someone's head
Fill-nor-fall - refers to someone or something lost, similar to 'head nor tail'
Flam - (1) to deceive or cheat (2) a lie or falsehood
Flick - the fur of a rabbit, cat or other animal
Flinder - butterfly
Flinder-mouse or **flitter-mouse** - bat
Flue - delicate, sickly or weak
Fluff - anger, choler
Folkestone beef - dried dogfish
Folkestone girls or **Folkestone lasses** - heavy rainclouds
Foreigner - anyone who was not born in Kent
Frail - (1) a flail (2) a small basket (3) peevish

F

Frape - (1) to worry, fuss or fidget (2) a woman of anxious temperament
Frimsy - slight, thin, soft
Frith - hedge, woodland or coppice
Furrick or **furrige** - to forage, rummage

G

Gaffer - a master
Gagey - of the weather, uncertain or showery
Galligaskins - trousers
Gance or **gause** - thin, gaunt, slender
Gavelkind - ancient system of land tenure in Kent
Gifts - white specks in the fingernails; supposedly an omen of future events
Gill - small, wooded valley with a stream
Gimmer - mistress, female employer
Goff - apple
Goyster - to laugh in a loud and vulgar manner
Gracious-heart-alive - an exclamation of complete astonishment
Granable - very
Grip - a dry ditch or a drainage furrow
Grizzle - to complain or grumble
Guesting - gossiping

H

Hagged - thin, gaunt, haggard
Hagister - magpie
Halm, hame, haulm or **helm** - stubble that is gathered after the corn has been carried
Hanger - a hanging wood on the side of a hill
Hank - a skein of thread or silk
Happy-ho - coincidental or similar
Hardhewer - stonemason
Hasty - violent, heavy (of rain etc.)
Hatch up - to prepare for
Hawmell - a small close or paddock
Heart-grief - great grief
Heaver or **hever** - a crab
Heft - the weight of something
Helving - gossiping
Hem - a word used for emphasis; very, exceedingly
Hern, herne or **hernshaw** - a heron
Hicket - to hiccup
Hike - to drive (someone) away, turn (someone) out
Hobbled - confused, puzzled, baffled
Hockatty kick - a lame person
Hocker-headed - passionate, fretful
Hog-headed - stubborn, obstinate
Holt - a wood
Hommucks - big, awkward feet
Hop-dog - (1) a caterpillar (2) a tool for removing hop poles from the ground
Hope - an anchorage for ships
Hopkin - a worker's supper following the hop-picking
Horn - a corner
Hornicle - hornet or dragonfly

H

Horse emmets - large ants
Hotch - to move awkwardly
Hovel - a piece of good fortune
Huffle - a feast or marry gathering
Huge or **hugy** - very
Hurr - sour, harsh, tart, crude
Hussle - to wheeze, breathe roughly
Hussy - to rub the hands together when cold

I

Ikey - proud, arrogant
In 'opes - hopeful (East Kent)
Inkspewer - cuttlefish
Innocent - small and attractive
Interrupt - to annoy, interfere with
Itch - (1) to be very anxious (2) to creep

J

Jack up - to give up, stop, finish doing something
Jawsy - garrulous, talkative
Jock - to jolt
Jockey - rough, uneven
Joskin - a farm labourer or driver engaged to one master
for the whole year
Just - very, extremely

Chalk pit and lime kilns, Blue Bell Hill, Maidstone.
Maidstone Museum

K

Karfe - the cut made by a saw or axe
Keen - a weasel
Keep-all-on - persevere, press on with, continue
Keg-meg - a gossip or newsmonger
Kick-up-jenny - an old public house game using ninepins
Kindley - productive, fertile
Kippered - of skin, chapped, cracked and sore
Kittle - to tickle
Knucker - to neigh

L

Lace - to flog, whip or beat
Lady-keys - flowers - either cowslips or wild arum
Lain - a thin coat of snow on the ground
Last - (1) ten thousand herrings (2) an ancient court on Romney Marsh

L

Latchetty - loose, falling to pieces
Lather - ladder
Leather - to beat, belabour
Leavener - elevenses, or any light snack between meals
Lees - a piece of common ground or pasture
Leety - slovenly, slow
Lief-coup or **litcop** - an auction of goods from a house or business
Limb - a naughty or mischievous child
Linger - to long or pine for
Lingy - idle, loitering
Lirry - a blow to the ear or side of the head
Lither - supple, limber, pliant
Lompy - clumsy, fat, awkward
Love - a widow
Lushington - a habitual drinker or drunkard
Lusty - flourishing, in good order, healthy

M

Mabbled - confused, puzzled, mixed up
Maggoty - unreliable, restless, whimsical
Man-sucker - cuttlefish
Marm - jelly
Marygold or **merrigo** - a ladybird
Match-a-running or **match-running** - a children's game similar to Prisoner's Base but unique to Kent
Maudring - mumbling
Maunder - (1) to scold or complain (2) to wander around aimlessly

M

Maxhill, maxon, maxul, misken or **mixon** - a dungheap

May Hill - used of someone ill, in the sense that they will not 'get up May Hill', i.e. live beyond May

May-bug - a cockchafer (also called a July-bug)

Meach or **meecher** - to creep about quietly

Meakers, meece or **mickies** - mice

Measure for a new jacket - to flog or beat

Measuring-bug - caterpillar

Meen - to shiver slightly

Mendment(s) - manure, droppings

Merciful - blessed (used as an intensive expletive)

Milch-hearted - kind-hearted, mild, timid

Misery - bodily (rather than mental) pain

Misword - an angry or abusive word

Mizmaze - puzzle, confusion, mishmash

Modren - mothers

Mort - a large quantity, abundance

Muddle about - to do a little amount of work to keep oneself occupied, to potter

N

Nabbler - a mischief-maker, an argumentative person

Ne'er a once - not once

Neighbour - to associate with

Newland - newly ploughed land

Nickopit - a bog or quagmire; a hole in a dyke

Nisy - simpleton, ninny

Nod - the nape of the neck

Nohow - not at all, no way
Noration - a fuss, row or disturbance
Nuncheon - a midday meal
Nurity - goodness, nourishment

Hop Garden - The Bin, taken around 1907.
Maidstone Museum

O

Oast - kiln for drying hops
Obedience - a bow or curtsey
(Be) off from - prevent, avoid
One-eyed - (1) inconvenient (2) cock-eyed
Oo - to feel 'all of an oo' is to feel unwell or confused
Ood - seaweed or wood
Ornary or **ornery** - ordinary; inferior, common or bad
Otherwhere-else - somewhere else
Otherwhile - occasionally, now and then

O

Outface - to withstand, resist or defy
Out-of-doors - no longer fashionable
Outroope - an auction of household goods
Outrunnings - a straggling piece of woodland beyond the defined boundary

P

Palter - to steal from wrecked ships and their crews
Pandle - a shrimp
Parock - a meeting in the Weald of Kent to assess rents and pannage
Pattern - to imitate or copy
Pea-bug or **peasie-bug** - woodlouse
Peart - lively, energetic, brisk
Pedigree - a long, rambling story
Peeky - unwell or ill-looking
Peggy-washdish - the water wagtail
Pell - a deep section of a river or a hole in the riverbed
Perk - to fidget restlessly
Pester up - to harass, bother or crowd
Peter Grievous - a fretful, whining or complaining person
Pikey - originally a traveller on the turnpike; hence a vagabond or ruffian
Pimp - a small bundle of cut wood used to light fires
Pisen - peas
Pitter - to loosen earth or throw it gently up
Pittering iron - an iron poker

P

Planets - rain 'by planets' means a localised shower rather than widespread rain

Platty - (1) scattered, uneven (2) (of a child) thin and sickly

Playstool - an area of land that was formerly parish property; previously a public recreation ground

Plog - to hinder, clog, block or retard

Plump - hard or dry

Poach - to tread holes in the ground (as cattle do in wet ground)

Poke or **pook** - a sack; also a bag used to transport hops from the garden to the oast

Polrumptious - rude, obstreperous

Polt - bold, audacious

Ponger, pung or **punger** - edible crab

Poochy - a bathe or paddle in shallow water

Print - bright, clear, light enough to read by

Prole - to prowl; to stroll

Pucker - a state of excitement or high temper

Pull-back - a hindrance or drawback

Purty tight - fairly well

Putch - a puddle; a water-filled hole

Q

Quant - a young oak sapling

Queer - to puzzle; to make (someone) feel strange or confused

Quiddy - brisk, lively

Q

Quilly - a prank or caper
Quitter for quatter - one thing in return for another, tit for tat

R

Racksened - overrun with
Raddle - a green stick, used to make wattles or hurdles
Rade - occurring early, ahead of time
Radical - a troublemaker or rebel
Rafe - a rush, a hurry
Raff - spoil, plunder, booty
Rammed - used as a milder alternative for 'damned'
Rapid - (of pain) violent or severe
Rasty or **reasty** - rancid, rank
Raw - angry
Reemer - anything considered to be of good quality
Reffidge - worthless, good for nothing
Regular - quite, fairly, somewhat
Ride - if something rides on the stomach it is hard to digest
Rights - to do something 'to rights' is to do it thoroughly; to 'go to rights' is to take the shortest route
Rip - a basket or pannier
Rivance - the last place where a person lived
Roil - to cause a distubance
Romance - to tell tall tales, to exaggerate
Rookery - a general dispute or heated altercation
Rough - a small area of neglected woodland
Royster - to play noisily and roughly

R

Ruckle - a struggle
Ruggle-about - to move or walk about only with difficulty
Run-a-head - to be delirious
Rusty - bad-tempered, crabby

S

Saime - lard
Salts, salterns or **saltings** - marshy land on the coast, which is covered at high tide
Sare - rotten, faded, worn
Sartin - steadfast, sure, certain, stern or severe
Scaddle or **sceddle** - wild, mischievous
Scimminger - a counterfeit coin
Scithers - scissors
Scoase - to swap or exchange
Scran - a small amount of food taken into the field by a worker
Scratch - to do something hurriedly or hastily
Scratch along - to make a bare living in difficult times
Scrooch - to make a scraping noise
Scrooge or **scrouge** - to push, squeeze or crowd
Scrow - a bad-tempered, peevish person
Sculch or **scultch** - rubbish; or unhealthy things eaten by children
Searse - to strain or sift
Sessions - a disturbance or fuss
Set-out - a great event or disturbance
Sew - (to) dry

S

Shadder or **shatter** - to fear, be afraid of
Sharn bug - stag beetle
Sheer - bright, clear or pure
Sheeres or **shires, the** - all parts of the world other than Kent, Sussex and Surrey
Shell-fire - phosphoresence from decayed straw or wood
Shent or **shunt** - to reproach or chide
Shide - a plank or board
Shockled or **shrockled** - shrivelled, shrunken, wizened
Shows for - looks like
Shrape or **shreap** - to scold or chide
Shuckish - shifty, uncertain, unreliable
Sight - a large quantity or number of something
Skent - to scowl
Skut - to crouch down
Slack - undercooked or underdressed
Slagger - to limp or walk slowly
Slop - a rough smock worn over their clothes by workmen
Smoult - hot, sultry
Smug - to steal
Snob - cobbler
Some-one-time - now and then, occasionally
Soss - a mess
Spaddle or **spandle** - to shuffle in walking; to make dirty or untidy
Spalt - impudent, heedless
Spry - a broom for sweeping a barn floor
Stadel, stale or **stath** - rung of a ladder
Starf take you! - a curse or oath on someone ('starf' comes from the Anglo-Saxon for a plague)

S

Staunch - to walk heavily and clumsily
Stilt - a crutch
Stoach - to stamp around in muddy ground
Stodger - a sturdy, strong fellow
Stolt - brisk, hearty
Strooch - to drag the feet, to slouch or shuffle
Stunt - obstinate, dogged, sullen
Sturm - morose, sullen
Sundays and worky-days - i.e. all the days of the week, if someone's work took up all their waking hours
Sun-dog or **sun-hound** - a halo around the sun, supposedly a forecast of rain
Swelked - overcome by the heat
Swimmy or **swimy** - dizzy, faint or giddy

T

Tack - an unpleasant taste
Taffety - squeamish or particular about food etc.
Tarnal - a strong expletive, usually denoting something very bad (from 'eternal')
Tatter, tattery or **tatty** - bad-tempered, peevish
Ted or **teddy** - to make hay by tossing and spreading it in the sun
Tedious - excessively, violently, very
Tetaw - fool, simpleton
Thick-thumbed - clumsy, awkward, untidy, slovenly
Thrible - treble, threefold
Thunderbug - midge

T

Thurrock - a wooden drain under a gate or bank
Tie - a foot-race between two competitors
Tiene or **tyene** - anger
Tilter - condition, fitness (as in 'out of tilter')
Tip-tongued - unclear in speech, inarticulate, lisping
Tither - to trifle, waste time
To and-agin - to and fro, back and forth
Tommy - a workman's lunch
T'other day - the day before yesterday
To-year - this year
Twink - a shrewish or grasping woman

U

Uncous or **unky** - melancholy, downhearted, lonely
Unthrum - awkward, inconvenient

V

Vast - very, exceedingly (often used of very small things)
Vigilous - angry, fierce, vicious

W

Wacker - (1) active, lively (2) angry
Wankle - sickly, in poor health (usually of a child)
Weald - formerly the Weald was the wooded part of Kent
Welter - to wither, wilt
Went - a path or way
Whatsay? - what did you say?
Whicket for whacket - tit for tat
Whiffle or **wiffle** - to blow in gusts
Whilk - to complain, mutter
Whip-sticks - quickly, directly
Whist - silent, quiet
Whitter - to mutter or complain
Winder - to whimper
Workish - industrious, hard-working
Wrongtake - to misunderstand

Y

Yaffle - the green woodpecker
Yaffle, yoffle or **yuffle** - (1) to eat or drink noisily
Yar - brisk, nimble, quick
Yaugh - dirty, filthy, nasty

Z

Zeterday - Saturday
Zoster - sister

ORIGINS OF AND LITTLE-KNOWN FACTS

ABOUT THE KENT DIALECT

The History of Kentish Dialect

Kent's position as the nearest part of the British Isles to our European neighbours played an important part in the evolution of its dialect. The name 'Kent' itself appears to date from Celtic times, before the Anglo-Saxons arrived and long before the Norman Conquest. The best suggestion for its origin is that it derives from the word *canto*, meaning border, rim or edge. Thus Kent is, aptly, 'the land on the border'.

Julius Caesar wrote that the people of Kent were 'by far the most civilised inhabitants' of Britain, and who are we to argue? Perhaps it was the inevitable contact with the Germanic peoples across the Channel that helped in this 'civilising', and the growth of trade from the Roman period onwards must inevitably have led to overseas influences.

Chaucer and Kentish Dialect

Geoffrey Chaucer was born in the 1340s and died in 1400, and came to be known as 'the Father of English Literature'. Although he was not himself a Man of Kent, having been born in London, the form of English that he spoke – and wrote – was very much influenced by the dialect of the county.

Chaucer is of course best known today for *The Canterbury Tales*, in which his pilgrims tell stories to pass the time on their journey to the shrine of Saint Thomas à Becket at Canterbury Cathedral. Although they gather at the Tabard Inn in Southwark, in London, which was once part of Surrey, they are soon across the border.

Among the many Kentish words that are found in Chaucer are *brock* (a horse of inferior quality), *haw* (used with reference to a churchyard, although it can mean any small enclosed yard), *taas* (also 'tarse', meaning a heap or pile), and *youl* (to howl).

The Pilgrims' Way passes through Wrotham on its way to Canterbury.
Snodland Museum

Invicta

Every Kentish Man and Man of Kent takes pride in his county's motto – *Invicta*.

The meaning of the Latin motto is 'unconquered', and it is claimed by Kent because of the county's resistance to the Norman invaders led by William the Conqueror. Before William came ashore with his army on the coast of Sussex, the invaders had attempted a landing at Romney, but the local forces had stood firm against them.

HM Dockyard in Sheerness around 1880. A magnificent old wooden warship can be seen in the foreground of the picture. Maidstone Museum

Kentish Provincialisms

Parish and Shaw's invaluable *Dictionary of the Kentish Dialect* of 1887 records not only individual dialect words but also many of the 'provincialisms' and colourful turns of phrase used by the Kentish speaker. Some of these relate to traditions and superstitions, while others arise out of ways of life that have long since disappeared. The descriptions that follow are taken or adapted from the *Dictionary*.

Traditions and superstition

Banyan Day - This was a sailors' term for a day when no meat was served – 'Saddaday is a banyan-day.' 'What do 'ye mean?' 'Oh! a day on which we eat up all the odds and ends.'

Burr - The halo or circle round the moon is so called, e.g. 'There was a burr round the moon last night.' The weather-wise in East Kent will tell you, 'The larger the burr the nearer the rain.'

Championing - The lads and men who go round as mummers at Christmastide, singing carols and songs, are said to go championing. Probably the word is connected with St George the Champion, who is a leading character in the Mummers play.

Fairisies - Fairies. This reduplicated plural of fairy gives rise to endless mistakes between the fairies of the story-books and the Pharisees of the Bible!

Fairy-Sparks - Phosphoric light, sometimes seen on clothes at night, and in former times attributed to the fairies. Otherwise called 'shell-fire'.

Gooding - The custom of going about asking for gifts on St Thomas's Day, 21 December. Still kept up in many parts of Kent.

Guestling - The ancient court of the Cinque Ports, held at Shepway, near Hythe, and other places.

Hodening or Hoodening - The name formerly given to a mumming or masquerade, a custom formerly prevelant in Kent on Christmas Eve; it is now discontinued, but the singing of carols at that season is still called hodening.

Holly-Boys and Ivy-Girls - It was the custom on Shrove Tuesday in West Kent to have two figures in the form of a boy and girl, made one of holly, the other of ivy. A group of girls engaged themselves in one part of the village in burning the holly-boy, which they had stolen from the boys, while the boys were to be found in another part of the village burning the ivy-girl, which they had stolen from the girls, the ceremony being, in both cases, accompanied by loud huzzas.

Horn Fair - An annual fair held at Charlton, in Kent, on St Luke's Day, the 18th of October. It consists of a riotous mob, who, after a printed summons, disperse through the adjacent towns, meet at Cuckold's Point, near Deptford, and march from thence, in procession through that town and Greenwich to Charlton, with the horns of different kinds upon their heads; and, at the fair, there are sold ram's horns, and every sort of toy made of horn; even the gingerbread figures have horns. It was formerly the fashion for men to go to the Horn Fair in women's clothes.

Longtails - An old nickname for the natives of Kent.

Lorry, Lerry or **Lurry** - Jingling rhyme; spoken by mummers and others.

Popeing - To go popeing is to go round with Guy Fawkes on the 5th of November. 'Please, sir, remember the old Pope.'

Remembering - To go round with Guy Fawkes on 5th November is also called remembering. 'George and me went round remembering and got pretty nigh fower and threepence.'

Seven-Whistlers - The note of the curlew, heard at night, is called by the fishermen the seven-whistlers: 'It's them long-billed curlews; but I never likes to hear them.'

Shoe-Money - When strangers pass through a hop-garden their shoes are wiped with a bundle of hops, and they are expected to pay their footing, under penalty of being put into the basket. The money so collected is called shoe-money, and is spent on bread and cheese and ale, which are consumed on the ground the last day of hopping. The custom of wiping the shoes of passers-by is also practised in cherry orchards in the neighbourhood of Faversham and Sittingbourne.

The toll bridge and barbican at Sandwich.
Snodland Museum

Whispering The Death Of A Person – It was recorded in Eastry, near Sandwich, that when the master or mistress dies, or other members of a family, where bees are kept, it is customary for someone to go to the hives and whisper to the bees that the person is dead. The same custom has been observed with regard to cattle and sheep.

Gavelkind

After William the Conqueror took the throne in 1066 he imposed Norman rule throughout England; except for Kent, that is. After an altercation with the Men of Kent (and the Kentish Men) near Swanscombe he came to a mutually satisfactory agreement – he would allow Kent to retain its existing Anglo-Saxon laws in return for control of Dover Castle.

So it was that Kent remained unconquered, and while Norman feudal laws were imposed in the rest of the country the old ways and customs were maintained in the county. One of the most important of these was the system of land tenure known as *gavelkind*. Under this system, a man's land was divided among all his sons, or those of a brother who died without offspring would be divided among his brothers. The main difference between *gavelkind* and the Norman system was that the Normans recognised primogeniture – that the first-born would inherit the whole estate.

Swan Street in West Malling.
Snodland Museum

Amazingly, *gavelkind* remained in force in Kent for another 850 years, until 1925, when it was finally legally abolished by the Law of Property Act.

Household words

Boulting-Tub - A tub in which pork is pickled.

Bucking Chamber - A room in which the clothes were bucked, or steeped in lye (i.e. caustic soda), preparatory to washing.

Buck-Wash - A great washing-tub, formerly used in farm-houses, when, once a quarter, they washed the clothes of the farm servants, soaking them in strong lye.

Cob-Irons - Andirons; irons standing on the hearth, and intended to keep the brands and burning coals in their place; also the irons by which the spit is supported.

Cove - A shed; a lean-to or low building with a shelving roof, joined to the wall of another; the shelter which is formed by the projection of the eaves of a house acting as a roof to an outbuilding.

Covel - A water tub with two ears.

Coverlyd or **Covertlid** - The outer covering of the bed which lies above the blankets; a counterpane.

Crock - An earthen pan or pot, to be found in every

kitchen, and often used for keeping butter, salt, etc. It is a popular superstition that if a man goes to the place where the end of the rainbow rests he will find there a crock of gold.

Crup - (1) The crisp, hard skin of a roasted pig, or of roast pork (crackling); (2) A crisp spice-nut; (3) A nest - 'There's a wapses crup in that doated tree.'

Do - To 'do' for anyone is to keep house for him.

Dover House - A 'necessary house'.

Fleeting Dish - A shallow dish for cream.

Stuppin or **Stuppnet** - A stew-pan or skillet.

Tamsin - A little clothes horse, or frame, to stand before a fire to warm a shirt or a shift, or child's linen. Tamsen, Thomasin, Thomasine, is a woman's name, and is here used as though the 'horse' did the work of the servant of that name, For the same reason it is otherwise called a maid, or maiden. It is not only called Tamsin, but Jenny, Betty, Molly, or any other maiden name; and if it is very small it is called a girl.

Food and drink

Currantberries - currants.

Dollop - (1) A parcel of tea sewn up in canvas for

The Abbey Brewery at West Malling.
Snodland Museum

smuggling purposes; (2) A piece, or portion, of anything, especially food. 'Shall I give ye some?' 'Thankee, not too big a dollop.'

Folkestone Beef - Dried dogfish

Glimigrim - Punch.

Harcelet or **Harslet** - The heart, liver and lights of a hog.

Farming and agriculture

Binder - A long stick used for hedging; a long, pliable stick of any kind; thus, walnuts are thrashed with a binder. Also

A hop garden near Maidstone in 1907.
Maidstone Museum

applied to the sticks used in binding on the thatch of houses or stacks. 'They shouted fire, and when Master Wood poked his head out of the top room window, they hit him as hard as they could with long binders, and then jumped the dyke, and hid in the barn.'

Bobbin - A bundle of firewood (smaller than a fagot, and larger than a pimp), whereof each stick should be about 18 inches long. Thus, there are three kinds of firewood – the fagot, the bobbin and the pimp.

Bobbin-Tug - A light framework of wheels, somewhat like a timber-wagon, used for carrying bobbins about for sale. It has an upright stick at each of the four corners, to keep the bobbins in their places.

Bud - A weaned calf that has not yet grown into a heifer. So called, because the horns have not grown out, but are in the bud.

Bullock - A fatting beast of either sex.

Bunting - The bunting house is the outhouse in which the meal is sifted, while a *bunting-hutch* is the bin in which meal is bunted or bolted.

Caving - In West Kent, the refuse of beans and peas after threshing, used for horse-meat, but called *torf* or *toff* in East Kent.

Coupling Bat - A piece of round wood attached to the bit (in West Kent), or ringle (in East Kent), of two plough horses to keep them together.

Court Faggot - This seems to have been the name, anciently given, to the best and choicest faggot.

Cow Crib - The square manger for holding hay, etc., which stands in the straw-yard, and so is constructed as to be low at the sides and high at the corners.

Crow - The fat adhering to a pig's liver; hence, 'liver and crow' are generally spoken of and eaten together.

Cuckoo Corn - Corn sown too late in the spring.

Doels - The short handles which project from the bat of a scythe, and by which the mower holds it when mowing. The several parts of the scythe are: a) the scythe proper, or cutting part, of shear steel; b) the trai-ring and trai-wedge by which it is fastened to the bat; c) the bat or long staff, by which it is held when sharpening, and which is cut peeked, so that it cannot slip; and d) the doles, as above described.

Dog or **Hop-Dog** - An instrument for getting up hop-poles, called in Sussex a pole-putter.

Doings - Odd jobs. When a person keeps a small farm, and works with his team for hire, he is said to do doings for people.

Draught - The bar, billet, or spread-bat, to which the traces of all horses are fixed when four are being used at plough.

Drawhook - In East Kent, an implement for cleaning out dykes, and freeing them of weeds, consisting of a three-tined fork, bent round so as to form a hook, and fitted to a long handle.

Draw-Well - A hole or well sunk for the purpose of obtaining chalk.

Dyster - The pole of an ox-plough.

Earing - Ploughing.

Eend - A term in ploughing; the end of a plough-furrow. Two furrows make one eend. Always pronounced with a long 'ee'. 'I ain't only got two or three eends today, to finish the field.'

Flicking-Tooth-Comb - A comb for a horse's mane.

Fold-Pitcher - An iron implement, otherwise called a *peeler*, for making holes in the ground, wherein to put wattles or hop-poles.

Fore-Acre or **Forical** - The headland; the land at the ends of the field where the furrows cross.

Gamble or **Gambrel Stick** - A stick used to spread open and hang up a pig or other slaughtered animal.

Garbage - A sheaf of corn (Latin *garba*); a cock of hay; a faggot of wood, or other bundle of the product or fruits of the earth.

Gig - A billet, or spread bat, used to keep the traces of plough horses apart.

Glean - A handful of corn tied together by a gleaner.

Harvester - A stranger who comes into the parish to assist in the harvest.

Hemwoods - Part of a cart-horse's harness which goes round the collar, and to which the tees are fixed; called *aimes (hames)* in West Kent.

Hop-Spud - A three-pronged fork, with which the hop grounds are dug.

Horse - The arrangement of hop-poles, tied across from hill to hill, upon which the pole-pullers rest the poles, for the pickers to gather the hops into bins or baskets.

Lash-Horse or **Losh-Horse** - The third horse from the plough or wagon, or horse before a pinhorse in the team (East Kent).

Lubber Hole - A place made in a haystack when it is three-parts built, where a man may stand to reach the hay from the men in the wagon, and pitch it up to those on the top of the stack.

Nidget - A shim or horse-hoe with nine irons, used for cleaning the ground between the rows of hops or beans.

Pea-Hook - The implement used in conjunction with a hink for cutting peas. It was like a rippinghook, only mounted on a longer handle.

Peeler - A round iron bar, used for making the holes into which hop-poles or wattles are placed.

Plash - To repair a live hedge, by cutting half through some of the stems near the ground and then bending the upper parts down, and keeping them so by means of hooked sticks driven into the bank.

Pritchel - An iron share fixed on a thick staff for making holes in the ground.

Quid - The cud, chewed by a cow.

Rod-Horse - A horse in the shafts or rods. The four horses of a team are called 1) the rod-horse; 2) the pin-horse; 3) the losh-horse; 4) the fore-horse.

Strike-Baulk - To plough one furrow and leave another.

Warps - Distinct pieces of ploughed land separated by the furrows.

An old windmill and oast house in Smarden near Ashford.
Maidstone Museum

Oast Houses

One of the images that is most associated with the county of Kent is the oast house, with its tall, pointed cowl. Once a common sight, they fell into disuse when the hop-drying process for which they were built became industrialised. However, many of the old oast houses have been converted into delightful homes, retaining their character and preserving these symbols of old Kent for future generations.

Hops, of course, are one of the most important ingredients used in the brewing of beer, and the widespread growing of hops was one of the reasons that Kent became known as 'The Garden of England'. The hops were spread out on the upper floors of the building, and hot air from a fire on the lowest floor was able to pass up through the hops and out of the distinctive cowl at the top. Traditional oast houses are circular (their shape was called a *roundle*), and the cowl could rotate as the wind changed direction to ensure the efficient drying of the hops.

Oast itself means 'a kiln for drying malt or hops', although Parish and Shaw note that in the Kentish dialect the word could originally refer to any sort of kiln or oven, saying that it originated from *bryk-host*, a brick-kiln, and was in use long before hop-growing began. More often, the dialect word used for a kiln was *kell*, and it was not unusual for *kell* to be used as a general term to refer to the oast house itself. The cowl was often shortened to *cow*, dropping the final 'l'.

Other dialect words related to hop growing include – *green-bag*, a bag in which hops were brought from the garden to the oast (sometimes also called a *poke* or *pook*); *hair*, a cloth that was placed above the fire in the oast; and *tongue*, which was the name given to the projecting part of the cowl which caused it to turn in response to the wind direction.

The Garden of England?

Kent takes pride in its status as 'The Garden of England'. So there was fury across the Weald and beyond in 2006 when a television channel claimed that North Yorkshire had usurped the title, matched only by the anger in Cornwall when Devon tried to claim the pasty.

But where does the title come from, and what does it mean?

For most people it reflects the abundance of crops and plants that thrive in Kentish soil, from fields of fragrant hops to orchards of ripe apples. Like the breadbasket of the American Midwest, Kent has historically supplied much of Britain's food needs.

The Bull Inn at Wrotham.
Snodland Museum

Plants and flowers

Canterbury Bells - The wild campanula (*Campanula medicus*).

Cuckoo Bread - The wood sorrel (*Oxalis acetosella*).

Cucko-Pint - The wild arum (*Arum maculatum*).

Cuckoo's Bread And Cheese - The seed of the mallow.

Culver Keys - The cowslip (*Primula veris*).

Devil-In-The-Bush - The flower otherwise called Love-in-the-mist (*Nigella damascena*).

Devil's Thread - A weed that grows out in the fields. among the clover; it comes in the second cut, but does not come in the first. Otherwise called Hellweed (*Cuscuta epithymum*).

Dogs' Daisy - The May weed (*Anthemis cotula*); so called, ''Cause it blows in the dog-days, ma'am.'

Dragon's Tongue - *Iris foetidissima*, the stinking iris.

Fatten - A weed.

Finkle - Wild fennel (*Foeniculum vulgare*).

Flig - Strands of grass.

Foal's Foot - Colt's foot (*Tussilago farfara*).

French May - The lilac (*Syringa vulgaris*), whether white or purple.

Gaskin - *Prunus avium*, a half-wild variety of the damson, common in hedgerows, and occasionally gathered to send to London, with the common kinds of black cherry, for the manufacture of 'port wine'.

Gatteridge Tree - Prickwood or spindle (*Euonymus europaeus*).

Gayzels - Blackcurrants or wild plums.

Goule - Sweet willow (*Myrica gale*).

Grandmother's Nigh - The flower called monk's hood or aconite (*Aconitum napellus*).

Horse Peppermint - The common mint (*Mentha sylvestris*).

Horsebuckle - The cowslip (*Primula veris*).

Horse-Knot - The knapweed (*Centaurea nigra*); sometimes also called hard-weed.

Jack In The Box - Reddish-purple, double polyanthus.

Keeklegs - The early purple orchid (*Orchis mascula*).

Kilk - Charlock (*Sinapis arvensis*), the wild mustard.

Money-In-Both-Pockets - The plant otherwise known as honesty (*Lunaria biennis*), or white satin-flower, as it is sometimes called from the silvery lustre of its large circular-shaped saliques, which, when dried, were used to dress up fire-places in summer and decorate the chimney-mantels of cottages and village inns.

Mother Of Thousands - see 'Hen and Chickens'.

None-So-Pretty - The name of the little flower, otherwise known as London pride (*Dianthus barbatus*).

Old Man - Southernwood (*Artemisia abrotanum*).

Our Saviour's Flannel - At Bridge , near Canterbury, this name is given to *Echium vulgare* [viper's bugloss] and at Faversham to *Verbascum thapsus* [common mullein].

Paigle or **Pegle** - Cowslip (East Kent).

Quick - Hawthorn, e.g. a quick hedge is a hawthorn hedge.

Quicken - The mountain ash (*Pyrus aucuparia*).

Rabbit's Mouth - The snapdragon (*Antirrhinum majus*).

Ragged Jack - Meadow lychnis or 'ragged robin' (*Lychnis flos-cuculi*).

Red Petticoat - The common poppy; sometimes also called red-weed.

Tar-Grass - The wild vetch (*Vicia cracca*).

Weasel Snout - The toadflax (*Linaria vulgaris*) (see also 'Hen and chickens').

Religion and worship

Dog-Whipper - The beadle of a church, whose duty it was, in former days, to whip the dogs out of church. The word frequently occurs in old churchwardens' accounts.

Great Church, The - The Cathedral at Canterbury is always so called at Eastry.

Saint's-Bell - A small bell, which is rung just before the service begins.

Brewing and baking

Charred - Drink that is soured in the brewing.

Peal or **Peel** - A long-handled, broad, wooden shovel, used for putting bread into the oven.

Scubbit - A wooden shovel. That form of scubbit now used by maltsters and hop driers has a short handle; that formerly used by farmers for moving corn on the barn floor, prior to the introduction of the threshing machine, had a long handle.

Water, boats and fishing

The harbour at Whitstable.
Maidstone Museum

Bawley - A small fishing smack used on the coasts of Kent and Essex, around the mouth of the Thames and Medway.

Chop-Sticks - Cross-sticks to which the lines are fastened in pout-fishing. 'Two old umbrella iron ribs make capital chop-sticks.' – F. Buckland.

Doling - A fishing boat with two masts, each carrying a sprit-sail. Boys, in his *History of Sandwich*, speaks of them as 'ships for the King's use, furnished by the Cinque Ports'.

Eel-Sheer - A three-pronged spear for catching eels.

Foying - Victualling ships; helping them in distress, and acting generally as agents for them.

Griping - The name given in North Kent to the operation of groping at arm's length in the soft mud of the tidal streams for dabs and flounders.

Heaf - The gaff-hook used by fishermen at Folkestone.

Hoveler - A hoveler's vessel. A Deal boatman who goes out to the assistance of ships in distress. The hovelers also carry out provisions, and recover lost anchors, chains and gear. They are first-rate seamen, and their vessels are well built and well manned.

Kidels - Fishing nets (West Kent).

Kipper-Time - The close season for salmon, 'between the Feast of the Invention of the Cross (14 Sept) and the Epiphany (6 Jan)'.

Oare - Seaweed; seawrack. This is the name of a parish in North Kent, near Faversham, which is bounded on the north by the River Swale, where probably great quantities of seeweed were collected.

Peck - A heading knife, used by fishermen.

Ran - A Folkestone herring net, which is about thirty yards long, is made of four rans deep; and there are sixty meshes to a ran.

Snoods - Fishing lines. The lines laid for ness-congers are seventy-five fathoms long, and on each line are attached, at right angles, other similar lines called the snoods; twenty-three snoods to each line, each snood nine feet long (Folkestone).

The Cinque Ports

Part of the deal with William the Conqueror that left Kent unconquered – *invicta* – involved allowing the Normans to fortify Dover. Over the next century four other ports – Hastings in Sussex and Hythe, New Romney and Sandwich in Kent – joined Dover to form the 'Cinque Ports'. Taking their name from the Norman French for 'five', the ports played a vital role in coastal defence and the development of the Royal Navy.

Today the Confederation of the Cinque Ports is a purely ceremonial title, and two of the original ports – New Romney and Sandwich – are no longer even on the coast as a result of silting, erosion and other changes to the coastline. Following the death of The Queen Mother in 2002, the former First Sea Lord Admiral Michael Boyce became Lord Warden of the Cinque Ports.

Freemen of the Ports were known as *portsmen*, and under the feudal system were deemed to have the rank of baron. A number of words unique to the Cinque Ports were recorded in Parish and Shaw's *Dictionary of the Kentish Dialect* of 1887, such as the *bodar*, an officer who had the duty of arresting debtors and imprisoning them in Dover Castle;

An old photograph of Dover's impressive Western Docks.
Maidstone Museum

and a *doling*, which was a two-masted fishing boat which the Ports would keep available for use by the king. The Cinque Ports' court was called the *guestling*, reportedly because the first such meeting took place in the village of Guestling.

The name of the ports is pronounced 'sink' rather than in the style of modern French, and a quotation from the Confederation of the Port of Hythe's website shows how seriously this is taken –

'*Who names us SANK and not our SINK is forever a foe. His ships be engaged and after Bloody Battle SUNK. No prisoners be taken!*'

Ranks and titles

Borsholder - A head-borough; a petty-constable; a constable's assistant.

Court - The manor house, where the court leet of the manor is held. Thus, Eastry Court is the old house, standing on the foundations of the ancient palace of the Kings of Kent, wherein is held annually the Court of the Manor of Eastry.

Goodman - An old title of address to the master of a house.

Goody - The title of an elderly widow, contracted from *goodwife*.

Land features

Borstal or **Bostal** - A pathway up a hill, generally a very steep one. At Whitstable there is a steep hill called Bostal Hill.

Dray - A word usually applied to places where there is a narrow passage through the slime and mud.

Droke - A filmy weed very common in standing water.

Dunes - Sand hills and hillocks, near the margins of the sea.

Eylebourne (or **Nailbourn**) - An intermittent spring.

Fright-Woods or **Frith** - (1) A hedge or coppice. (2) A thin, scrubby wood, with little or no timber, and consisting mainly of inferior growths such as are found on poor soils, intermixed with heath, etc. Though some of the old woods bearing this name may now, by modern treatment, have been made much thicker and more valuable, they are also still called, as of old, fright-woods, as the Fright Woods, near Bedgebury.

Gate - A way from the cliffs down to the sea – Ramsgate, Margate, Kingsgate, Sandgate, Westgate.

Hassock - A large pond.

Hatch - A gate in the roads; a half-hatch is where a horse may pass, but not a cart.

Newgate Gap, Cliftonville, from an old postcard.
Maidstone Museum

Homestall - The place of a mansion-house; the enclosure of ground immediately connected with the mansion-house.

Horse-Road - In Kent, a road is not divided as elsewhere, into the carriage-road and the foot-path; but into the horse-road and the foot-road.

Joclet - A small manor, or farm.

Lathe - A division of the county of Kent, in which there are five lathes, *viz.*, Sutton-at-Hone, Aylesford, Scray, St Augustine's and Shepway (Anglo-Saxon, *laeth*).

Lope-way - A private footpath.

Lowey - The ancient liberty of the family of Clare at Tunbridge, extending three miles from the castle on every side.

Lows - The hollows in marshland where the water stagnates.

Lyste-Way - A green way on the edge of a field.

Mennys or **Minnis** - A wide tract of ground, partly copse and partly moor; a high common; a waste piece of rising ground. There are many such in East Kent, as Swingfield Minnis, Ewell Minnis, etc.

Mewse - An opening through the bottom of a hedge, forming a run for game.

Ness - A promontory; a cape; a headland. Seen in place

Dredgers unloading at Sheerness.
Maidstone Museum

names as Dungeness, Sheerness, etc. French, Nez; Scandinavian, Naze. So the English sailors call Blanc Nez, opposite Dover, Blank-ness or Black-ness.

Polder - A marsh; a piece of boggy soil.

Reach - A creek.

Ripe - A bank; the sea shore, as Lydd Ripe. In East Kent, the village of Ripple derives its name from the same Latin word, *ripa*.

Roughit - A small wood.

Sole - A pond, or pool of water.

Staddle - A building of timber standing on legs or steddles, to raise it out of the mud. Poor dwellings of this kind were formerly common enough in small fishing towns, such as Queensborough.

Stone-Reach - A portion of stony field, where the stones for a considerable distance lie very much thicker than in any other part.

Stray - A winding creek.

Summer-Land - Ground that lies fallow all the summer.

Sump - A small cove; a muddy shallow. The Upper and Lower Sump in Faversham Creek are small coves near its mouth where fishing vessels can anchor. The word is the same as swamp.

Swatch - A channel, or water passage, such as that between the Goodwin Sands.

Toft - A messuage; a dwelling-house with the adjacent buildings and curtilage, and the adjoining lands appropriate to the use of the household; a piece of ground on which the messuage formerly stood.

Tye - An extensive common pasture.

Wence or **Went** - A way, or the centre of a cross-roads.

Romney Marsh – A World Apart

Romney Marsh sits astride the Kent/Sussex border and covers an area of around a hundred square miles. Like the Isle of Thanet, it may be part of Kent (and of Sussex too), but it is also a world apart. In East Kent, it is simply 'the Marsh'. Indeed, many around these parts will tell you that the Marsh is the 'fifth quarter' of the world – Europe, America, Africa, Asia . . . and Romney Marsh.

If you visit the Marsh you will begin to see their point. There is nowhere else quite like it. Much of the land has been reclaimed from the sea over hundreds of years. In the nineteenth century most of it was given over to sheep, but today, with a decline in livestock prices, there is more arable farming. The shingle headland of Dungeness is dominated by its nuclear power station, although it achieved equal fame as the home of the late film director Derek Jarman, who cultivated a unique garden on the stones outside his cottage.

The unique landscape of Romney Marsh has resulted in numerous words that either have a special local meaning or are not found anywhere else – *backsters* or *backstays*, for example, are flat pieces of wood attached to the shoes to cross the shingle of Dungeness, whereas elsewhere in Kent a *backstay* is more likely to be a pole supporting a fence; to *clat* a sheep is to remove the dirt and wool stuck between its legs; and a *last* was a special court set up in ancient times to levy rates for the preservation of the marshes.

The old lighthouse at Dungeness.
Lydd Museum Collection

The Isle of Sheppey

Whisper it if you're in East Kent but, unlike its rival 'island' of Thanet, the Isle of Sheppey is still genuinely an island. Its name is derived from the Anglo-Saxon *sceapige*, meaning 'island of sheep', which gives a clue to its history. However, as well as providing plenty of grazing the island has also played an important role in naval history, with Sheerness first becoming a Royal Navy dockyard in the seventeenth century.

As with all island races, the 'sons of Sheppey' are a proud breed; they may talk of crossing the Swale as 'going into England'. The Swale was reputedly first bridged during the reign of Edward I in the thirteenth century, but the

Beach scene at Sheerness.
Maidstone Museum

bridge was swept away and the island was accessible only by ferry until the 1860s.

The Isle of Thanet

At the north-eastern tip of the county is Kent's own Riviera, the Isle of Thanet. Once it really was an island, separated from the rest of the county by the Wantsum Channel. In ancient times the Channel was at least two miles wide, and in the eighth century was reported to be three furlongs across – around a third of a mile – and it was not bridged until the fifteenth century.

The people of Thanet still regard themselves as an island race. If you're ever told in East Kent that someone lives 'on the island' then you can be sure that their home is somewhere in Thanet. Then again, if someone in North Kent says the same thing then they're probably talking about the Isle of Sheppey!

Although the Wantsum Channel has long since silted up, Thanet's island origins are still reflected in the pride and independence of its people, although the pronunciation that was once typical of island-dwellers (such as *meece* for mice) is now sadly lost to history.

However, as Estuary English continues to spread across the south of England, there are some reports that the 'th' sound is being replaced by an 'f'; one researcher recorded that the Island was now known by some as 'Planet Fanet'! First an island, now a planet; what next for this unique corner of Kent?

Kentish Men or Men of Kent?

Kent is a large county, with almost half of its boundary not with any neighbouring county but with the sea. So it is no surprise that the county has a particular pride and spirit of independence, well represented in its motto – *invicta*.

Within Kent, however, there are also divisions, most notably the difference between a Kentish Man and a Man of Kent. The traditional border between East Kent and West Kent is the county's main river, the Medway, although some historians have argued that it originally fell further east, with Gillingham having once been in the western half.

The bridge over the River Medway at Aylesford, the traditional boundary between Kentish Men and Men of Kent.
Medway Archive Collection

What remains clear is that a man from East Kent is a Man of Kent, while his fellow from the West is a Kentish Man; the female equivalents are Maid of Kent and Kentish Maid. Woe betide any 'furriner' who confuses one with the other!

Trades and professions

Collarmaker - A saddler who works for farmers; so called, because he has chiefly to do with the mending and making of horses' collars.

Higgler - A middleman who goes round the country and buys up eggs, poultry, etc., to sell again. So called, because he higgles or haggles over his bargains.

Looker - One who looks after sheep and cattle grazing in the marshes. His duties with sheep are rather different from those of a shepherd in the uplands.

Second-Man - Among farm servants there is a regular gradation of ranks; the first-man is the wagoner, par eminence, who has charge of the first team and is assisted by his 'mate', the second-man has charge of the second team and is assisted by his 'mate', and so on; while there is generally also a 'yard man', whose duty it is to look after the stock in the yard, and an odd man whose title, 'allworks', describes his duties. When a number of men are going along the road, with their respective teams the first man will be found leading, the second man next, and so on; each walking with his horses.

Margate – an Artists' Town

On the northern edge of the Isle of Thanet stands Margate. Sharing with its neighbours a pride in its 'island' status, Margate's history has inevitably been linked to the sea. As part of the expansion of the Cinque Ports in the fifteenth century it became a 'limb' of the main port of Dover, and it has long been a favourite resort of Londoners escaping the metropolitan bustle. Fishing has also been an important part of the local industry.

Today, however, Margate is gaining new renown as an artists' town. The great painter J.M.W. Turner first visited the town in 1786, when he was only ten or eleven years old, and would return many times thereafter. He told his friend, the writer and art critic John Ruskin, that 'the skies over Thanet are the loveliest in all Europe', and it was the quality of light – along with his close relationship with his landlady Mrs Booth – that brought him back to Margate time and time again.

In celebration of Turner's long association with the town, the Turner Contemporary Art Gallery was opened on Margate seafront in 2011, right on the spot where Mrs Booth's guest house once stood. As well as celebrating the work of Turner, the gallery will also provide a space to show contemporary works, including those of the latest famous artist to emerge from the town, Tracey Emin.

Strange Creatures of Kent

Kent has seen its fair share of strange and wonderful creatures, although some of them have remained frustratingly unseen. We have all heard tell of the Beast of Bodmin, but Kent too has its tales of flocks of sheep terrorised and slaughtered by mysterious night-time predators.

As long ago as 1905 there was a report of thirty sheep being killed by an unknown creature, an event that the writer Charles Fort considered to be 'paranormal'. In the same year, however, a further crop of killings was brought to an end when a hunting party shot and killed an escaped jackal that had been preying on local flocks.

More intriguing, perhaps, are the reports of supernatural creatures, notably the 'black dogs' and other hell hounds that have been encountered by the people of Kent. A motorist was alarmed when a huge black dog emerged from the fog near Pluckley, right into the path of his vehicle, only for the car to pass straight through the apparition.

Pluckley, near Ashford, has a reputation as the most haunted village in England, its spectres and apparitions including a ghostly highwayman and a gypsy woman who had been burned to death.

Animals, birds and other creatures

Dicky Hedge-Poker - The hedge sparrow.

Didapper or **Divedaper** - The dabchick.

Dishwasher - The water wagtail. Generally called 'Peggy Dishwasher'.

Dumbledore - A bumble bee.

Dun Crow - The hooded or Royston crow (*Corvus cornix*), which was once found in great numbers in North Kent during the winter.

Fazen - The fazen eel is a large brown eel, and is so called at Sandwich in contradistinction to the silver eel.

Fiddler - The angel, or shark-ray. 'We calls these fiddlers because they're like a fiddle.' The following couplet is from West Kent - 'Never a fisherman need there be, If fishes could hear as well as see.'

Fleck or **Flick** - Hares; rabbits; ground-game. 'They killed over two hundred pheasants, but not but terr'ble little fleck.'

Fly-Golding or **Golding** - A ladybird, also called a lady-cow.

Galls - Jellyfish.

Greybird - A thrush.

Hagister - A magpie.

Long-Dog - A greyhound.

Millers'-Eyes - Jellyfish (Dover).

Mollie - A hedge sparrow.

Monkey-Peas - A woodlouse.

Oxbird - The common dunlin (*Tringa variabilis*). Called 'Oxybird' in Sheppey.

Peggy - The water wagtail, also called 'Peggy Dishwasher' or 'Peggy Washdish'.

Post-Bird - The common spotted flycatcher (*Muscicapa grisola*).

Puttas or **Puttice** - A weasel or stoat.

Ruddock - A robin redbreast.

Screech-Owl - The common swift (*Cypselus apus*) (Sittingbourne).

Skip-Jack - The sand-hopper (*Talitrus saltator*) (Folkestone).

Tortoise - The cuttlefish (Folkestone).

Tuke - The redshank; a very common shore-bird on the Kentish saltings (Sittingbourne).

Twinge - An earwig.

Weather

Dolours - A word expressive of the moaning of the wind, when blowing up for rain.

Downward - The wind is said to be downwards when it is in the south.

Folkestone girls, lasses or **washerwomen** - The name given to heavy rainclouds.

Gagey - Uncertain; showery.

Galey - Boisterous; stormy.

Givey - The ground is said to be givey when the frost breaks up and the roads become soft and rotten.

Hasty - Heavy; violent. Often used of rain.

Heavenshard - Heavily; said of rain.

List - The condition of the atmosphere when sounds are heard easily.

Planets - It rains 'by planets' when showers fall in a small compass, in opposition to general rain.

Print - Bright; clear; starlight; light enough to read by. 'The night (or the moon) is very print.'

Shuckish - Shifty; unreliable; uncertain; tricky. 'Looks as though we be going to have a lot of this shuckish weather.'

Sun-Dog or **Sun-Hound** - A halo round the sun; seen when the air is very moist; generally supposed to foretell the approach of rain.

Upward - The wind is said to be upward when it is in the north, and downward when it is in the south. The north is generally esteemed the highest part of the world.

Waller'd - The wind.

Weather - Bad weather. ''Tis middlin' fine now; but there's eversomuch weather coming up.'

The Goodwin Sands

Some six miles off the Kent coast near Deal lie the near-legendary Goodwin Sands. Actually a series of sandbanks, which also includes the Brake Bank nearer the shore, the Sands are believed to have claimed more than two thousand ships.

For many years it was thought that the Sands were the remains of a third Kentish island named Lomea that had once rivalled Thanet and Sheppey, but that theory is now discredited. The name 'Goodwin' derives from Godwin, the eleventh-century Earl of Wessex, with another story of their origin saying that the island was lost to the sea because Godwin had failed to maintain its coastal defences.

In November 1703 the last 'Great Storm' before the famous one of 1987 (see 'The Great Storm') saw the loss of more than fifty ships in a single night, including four major ships of the line, at least thirteen men o'war and some forty merchant vessels. Sir Cloudesley Shovell, Admiral of the Fleet, must have thought this would be the worst naval disaster of his career, but some four years later he was to lose several more ships – and his own life – off the Isles of Scilly. More recently, the career of the pirate station Radio Caroline's final ship, the *MV Ross Revenge*, was brought to an end when she also ran aground on the sands in 1991.

Considering their fearsome reputation as a marine graveyard, it is perhaps strange that the Goodwin Sands have come to take on happier associations in popular culture. One of these is the tradition of playing cricket on the sands, which began in 1824 when the Ramsgate Harbourmaster, one Captain K. Martin, took two sides out at low tide. This remained an annual tradition until 2003, although the hazardous nature of the game was demonstrated when a television reconstruction for the BBC series *Coast* ended up requiring a rescue from the local lifeboat.

Readers of Ian Fleming's original novel *Chitty Chitty Bang Bang – The Magical Car* will recall the moment when the Pott family use their magical car to fly out to the Goodwin Sands for a picnic. Having fallen asleep, they are apparently trapped by the incoming tide, with no room to achieve a take-off, leaving them *threatened with mortal danger*! However, the magical car once again comes to their rescue, transforming into a speedboat (or, memorably, in the film version a colourful hovercraft) to effect their escape.

Another positive aspect of the Sands is that they act as a barrier that helps provide a safe refuge in The Downs, the area just off the East Kent coast, in bad weather; just as long as the ships avoid running aground first! Today the Goodwin Sands are guarded by a permanent lightship, which has taken over from the two on-shore lighthouses that previously marked its position, but they remain a fearsome obstacle to vessels navigating the Channel, especially in stormy weather when 'Old Waller'd' starts a-blowing.

Kentish Words in Shakespeare

The influence of Kentish on early printed English meant that words that were originally confined to Kent were spread more widely around the country. This is probably why a number of Kentish words (which may once have been found in standard English too) sometimes turn up in the works of Shakespeare. Some examples are:

bat - a stick or staff ('So slides he down upon his grained bat', *A Lover's Complaint*)

baven or **bavin** - a small bundle of brushwood ('The skipping king, he ambled up and down / With shallow jesters, and rash bavin wits / Soon kindled and soon burnt', *Henry IV, Part I*)

buck - a pile of laundry ready for washing ('They conveyed me into a buck-basket; rammed me in with foul shirts and smocks, socks, foul stockings, greasy napkins . . .', *The Merry Wives of Windsor*)

cade - a barrel containing six hundred herrings; any parcel, or quantity of pieces of beef, less than a whole quarter (Cade: 'We John Cade, so termed of our supposed father . . .' Dick [aside]: 'Or rather, of stealing a cade of herrings', *Henry VI, Part II*)

cantle - a portion or corner of something that is of indefinite dimensions ('See how this river comes me cranking in / And cuts me, from the best of all my land / A huge half moon, a monstrous cantle out', *Henry IV, Part I*)

court cupboard - a sideboard or cabinet used formerly to display the silver flagons, cups, beakers, ewers, etc., i.e., the family plate, and distinguished from the 'livery cupboard', or wardrobe ('Away with the joint-stools, remove the court cupboard, look to the plate', *Romeo and Juliet*)

cypress - a material like crape ('In sad cypress let me be laid', *Twelfth Night*)

ear - to plough ('Caesar, I bring thee word - Menecrates and Menas, famous pirates / Make the sea serve them, which they ear and wound / With keels of every kind', *Antony and Cleopatra*)

i fecks - a corruption of 'in faith' (a phrase used by Leontes in *A Winter's Tale*)

fardle - a bundle or pack ('Who would fardels bear / To grunt and sweat under a weary life?', *Hamlet*)

fear - frighten, i.e. cause fear rather than be afraid ('To see his face the lion walk'd along / Behind some hedge, because he would not fear him', *Venus and Adonis*)

gaberdine - a coarse loose frock ('You call me misbeliever, cut-throat dog, / And spit upon my Jewish gaberdine', *The Merchant of Venice*)

hearnshaw - heron (when Hamlet speaks of knowing 'a hawk from a handsaw' he is making a play on this word)

maund - a large, round, open wicker basket ('A thousand favours from a maund she drew, Of amber, crystal and of braided jet', *A Lover's Complaint*)

swath or **swarth** - a row of grass or corn, as it is laid on the ground by the mowers ('And there the strawy Greeks, ripe for his edge, Fall down before him like the mower's swath', *Troilus and Cressida*)

tedious - extreme, acute, long-lasting but not necessarily wearisome ('Within me grief hath kept a tedious fast', *Richard II*)

In *King Lear*, the virtuous Edgar disguises himself as 'mad Tom o' Bedlam' to avoid recognition, so it may be that Shakespeare has deliberately chosen to have him use dialect words as part of his pretence. At one point Edgar threatens Goneril's servant Oswald, saying, ' . . . ise try whether your costard or my ballow be the harder' – 'ballow' is an old Kentish word for a stick or cudgel, while 'costard', which means 'apple', is a mocking reference to Oswald's head! It's interesting to see that Shakespeare writes Edgar's lines using 'z' for 's' ('zir' and 'zwaggered', for example), suggesting that the character is deliberately using a Kentish accent as part of his disguise.

Seal village near Sevenoaks.
Snodland Museum

The Great Storm of 1987

BBC weatherman Michael Fish will never live it down. On 15 October 1987 he calmly announced to the nation that a woman had telephoned to say that she had heard reports that a hurricane was approaching. 'Don't worry,' he said, 'there isn't . . .' He did add, however, that it was going to get 'rather windy'.

In that at least he was correct. Later that evening the worst storm to hit south-east England for nearly 300 years arrived, and Kent bore the brunt of it. The town of

Sevenoaks lost six of the historic trees that gave it its name, among around fifteen million others that were brought down by winds that blew at around 80mph for several hours.

Damage was widespread and eighteen people tragically lost their lives that night. Fallen trees blocked roads and railways and power lines were brought down, while numerous boats were wrecked or capsized, including a passenger ferry that was driven aground.

A miscellany

Cats' brains - Ground overlying gravel with spots of sand in it.

Chummie - (1) A chimney sweep; (2) A house sparrow.

Dogs - Two pieces of wood connected by a piece of string, and used by thatchers for carrying up the straw to its place on the roof, when arranged for thatching.

Eche - An eke, or addition; as, an additional piece to a bell rope, to eke it out and make it longer. So we have Eche-End near Ash-next-Sandwich.

Everything something - Something of everything; all sorts of things. 'She called me everything something'; i.e. she called me every name she could think of.

Foy - A treat given by a person on going abroad or returning home. There is a tavern at Ramsgate called the Foy Boat.

Garreted - The phrase 'not rightly garreted' means something wrong in 'the top storey'. Spoken of a weak and silly person, whose brain is not well furnished.

Gentleman - A person who from age or any other cause is incapacitated from work. 'He's a gentleman now, but he just manages to doodle about his garden with a weedin'-spud.'

Horses - To 'set horses together' is to agree.

Middling - A word of several shades of meaning, from very much or very good, to very little or very bad. The particular sense in which the word is to be taken for the time is determined by the tone of the speaker's voice alone.

Miller's eye - To put the miller's eye out is when a person, in mixing mortar or dough, pours too much water into the hole made to receive it; then they say, 'I reckon you've put the miller's eye out now!' (Eastry).

Minute - A Kentish man would say 'a little minute', where another would say 'a minute'.

No ought - Ought not. 'The doctor said I no ought to get out.' The expression 'you ought not' is seldom used; it is almost invariably 'no ought'. A similar use of prepositions occurs in such phrases as 'up-grown', 'out-asked', etc.

No principle - This expression is only applied in Kent to people who do not pay their debts.

No sense - Nothing to speak of; nothing to signify. 'It don't rain; leastways, not no sense.'

Old - Parish and Shaw note that 'This word is constantly applied to anything or anybody without any reference to age.'

Order - To be 'in order' is a common expression for being in a passion. 'When the old chap knows them cows have been out in the clover he'll be in middlin' order; he'll begin to storm and no mistake!'

Play the band - Instead of saying 'The band is going to play', it is common to hear 'They are going to play the band.'

Prick up the ears - A proverbial saying is 'You prick up your ears like an old sow in beans.'

Further Reading

If this little book has whetted your appetite to learn more about Kentish dialect, then you will probably want to track down a copy of William D. Parish and William F. Shaw's *Dictionary of the Kentish Dialect and Provincialisms in Use in the County of Kent*, originally published in 1887 by the English Dialect Society but reprinted many times since and also available online.

The best online resource is the website of the Kentish Archaeological Society (www.kentarchaeology.ac). The site includes not only a copy of Parish and Shaw's *Dictionary* but also an excellent dictionary of Kentish dialect compiled by the Society in 2008 from a number of sources.

Other resources that have proven invaluable when writing this book include:

Books

David Crystal, *The Stories of English*, London: Allen Lane, 2004

Alan Major, *Kentish As She Wus Spoke*, Seaford: S B Publications, 2001

Websites

'The Kent Family Garden', Kent Online Parish Clerks, www.kent-opc.org

'Kenticisms', www.petrichor.net

Why on e

Hugo was ... hospital gown ... front of him, ... back of the chair and he looked every inch an invalid. Except for his determined expression.

'Mr Tallent, I'm busy,' Christie told him brusquely. 'Could you please return to your room? *Now!*'

'You're attempting a Caesarean on your own.'

'Yes, but what—'

'You can't do it alone. You need an anaesthetist.'

'I don't have one,' she snapped. 'Will you get back to bed?'

'You do have one,' Hugo told her, his eyes resting on hers. His look was steady, sure and strong, telling her that he spoke the absolute truth. 'And, no, I won't go back to bed. I'm a qualified anaesthetist and I'm here to help.'

Marion Lennox has had a variety of careers—medical receptionist, computer programmer and teacher. Married, with two young children, she now lives in rural Victoria, Australia. Her wish for an occupation which would allow her to remain at home with her children, her dogs, the cat and the budgie led her to attempt writing a novel. Marion also writes under the same name for Mills & Boon® Tender Romance™.

Recent titles by the same author:

A FOREVER FAMILY

DOCTOR ON LOAN

BY
MARION LENNOX

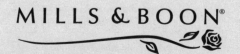

MILLS & BOON®

MILLS & BOON and MILLS & BOON with the Rose Device are registered trademarks of the publisher.

*First published in Great Britain 2001
Harlequin Mills & Boon Limited,
Eton House, 18-24 Paradise Road, Richmond, Surrey TW9 1SR*

© Marion Lennox 2001

ISBN 0 263 82649 X

*Set in Times Roman 10½ on 11½ pt.
03-0301-51545*

*Printed and bound in Spain
by Litografía Rosés, S.A., Barcelona*

CHAPTER ONE

SO THIS was heaven.

There were bright lights and too much white. A pain behind his eyes was dully threatening, but he could easily ignore it. Why? Because the most gorgeous woman he'd ever seen was smiling straight down at him.

She was young, he thought, but it was tough to tell how young and his brain wasn't up to deep thought. Her hair was a riot of glossy, shoulder-length brown curls and she had the most beautiful green eyes! Her pert nose sported just the right number of freckles, and her wide, warm smile was enough to kick a man sideways.

As for the rest... He let his confused mind drift as he took in the whole package. She was of middling height and deliciously curvy. Her clothes were simple—a crimson fisherman's guernsey and faded, figure-hugging jeans. The women in Hugo Tallent's life were normally more sophisticated than this, but it did her no harm in his eyes at all. In fact, he'd never seen a woman so lovely!

Especially since he'd expected to never see anything again. He'd expected to be dead.

'Hi, there. Ready to wake up?'

Her voice matched her smile—light and lovely—but maybe this wasn't heaven after all, he thought dazedly. The pain in his head was suddenly very, very real.

She saw it. The beautiful eyes, sea green and twinkling, creased in sympathy, and her hand took his. It was strong for a woman, and warm. It was infinitely reassuring.

'I've given you something for the pain. It'll take effect

5

soon. Don't fight it. Relax. Things are only going to get better.'

So, no, this wasn't heaven. This was a real, live, flesh and-blood woman, smiling down at him with sympathy and her loveliness was growing by the minute.

'*Things are only going to get better,*' she'd said. It was a good thought. As memory surfaced he tried to collect his bewildered thoughts, and he winced. Things could hardly be worse than they'd been the last time he'd been conscious. He hadn't expected to be here now, wherever he was.

Why wasn't he dead? Who had hauled him from his nightmare?

He looked up at the strange woman. Her eyes were still calmly watchful, and her hand still held his. This, then, was his saving angel and there was nothing for it but to offer his all.

'Marry me?' he asked.

The lovely eyes widened in astonishment. Whatever she'd been expecting, it wasn't this. Laughter flashed in but she didn't withdraw her hand. She was watching him as if she was expecting some sort of interesting symptoms. Brain damage?

'I beg your pardon?'

'If you pulled me out from under the boat...' His voice was a husky whisper, laced with pain, but it wasn't brain damage that was making him say what he was saying. He'd never meant anything so much in his life. 'If you hauled me from the sea... I'm offering my hand in marriage, half my worldly goods—no, dammit, you can have everything. Name it and it's yours.'

Her smile faded.

'It was no thanks to me that you were saved,' she told him softly, and the warmth was still in her voice, but with it was the shadow of the terrors of the night before. She hesitated, as if wondering whether he was fit enough to listen, and then decided to go on. 'Ben Owen and his mates were checking for prawns in the estuary when they saw our boat heading for the entrance. The estuary's sheltered but the harbour entrance certainly isn't. They thought they must be dreaming. To approach our harbour in last night's storm was suicidal.'

It was. He'd known that—too late. It would have been safer to head for the rocks.

'Ben risked his life to save you,' she told him, and there was the faintest trace of censure in her tone. 'He's fourteen years old. He dived under the boat and hauled you up, and God must have been watching over the pair of you. You're both complete dopes. You for trying to use the harbour and Ben for risking his life saving you. He's in the next ward.'

'The next ward.' That shook him, and for the first time he looked about him. Really looked. This was a ward? He was in hospital?

First things first. The throbbing pain in his head was easing a bit, letting him think.

'A boy…saved me? And he's here? He's hurt?' His words were clipped with fear. A fourteen-year-old—risking all to save him!

'He has a gashed hand and he's still suffering from shock,' she said quickly, watching his face. 'That's all. I gather you were caught in your safety harness under the boat. Ben wears his hunting knife everywhere, like a talisman. It's my belief he wears it to bed strapped over his pyjamas. He managed to cut you free but it took some doing.'

'And this was…underwater?'

'Yes. Underwater.'

'Dear God.' He closed his eyes and unconsciously his hand tightened on hers, taking comfort from the warmth of her touch. The realness of her. To come so close…

Stupid, stupid, stupid.

'Try not to think about it,' she said gently, and her fin gers disengaged. 'It's over and you're both safe. But…' Sh took a deep breath, dreading what she had to ask, but know ing she must. 'We didn't find anyone else. Was there any one with you in the boat? Please—'

'No.' That had been the whole problem. Damn his bab brother! But at least it *had* only been himself here. 'Ther was no one else.'

'Then you've been incredibly lucky,' she told him, sigh ing with relief. She could tell the searchers there were n bodies to find, and she'd been filled with dread all night 'You've had a crack on the head which I've stitched but i looks like causing no long-term damage. You've water on your lungs, which means you're staying right where yo are until we can clear it, you have enough bruises to mak you look interesting for weeks…and you dislocated you knee.'

'My knee.' For the first time he let himself think abou his body. The painkiller—whatever she'd given him—wa settling the throbbing to a dull ache. He assumed she' given him something earlier and had topped it up now, bu there was definitely pain all around. Including his left leg Maybe his leg was the worst, though it was competing har with his head. He tried to move his leg and it felt heavy and wooden.

'I've managed to put it back into position, and I'v strapped it,' she told him. 'But I'm afraid it's badly bruised and the swelling's still coming up. Don't try to move it As I said, you've been incredibly lucky.' She touched hi hand again, and the warmth went right through him. Th shock of the night was still with him and his need for hu man contact was almost overwhelming.

'I'm sorry, but I need to go,' she said. She looked aroun as the door opened and a nurse appeared. 'Mary-anne wil it with you for a bit and tell you all you need to know, but it's better if you sleep. Tell Mary-anne if the pain gets worse, or if you feel dizzy or ill.'

She hesitated then, unsure. 'What I'd really like is to send you to the mainland,' she admitted, 'but until this storm dies I'm afraid you're stuck with me. And with Grandpa. And Grandpa says you'll be fine so we'll just have to trust his judgement.'

And with another of her lovely smiles, a smile that contained just the faintest hint of anxiety, she took herself out of his room.

I should send him to Brisbane.'

Dr Stan Flemming was perched in his favourite chair in the nurses' station—a position where he could see everyone who came and went from Briman Island's tiny hospital. Since his stroke he spent most of his days here. Now he looked at his granddaughter from under craggy eyebrows and grimaced.

Christie was bone weary. She was twenty-eight years old, and this was no life for a woman. Or for anyone! She'd been up all night and the pressure was hardly likely to stop now. She took too much on herself. Trying to protect him...

It made him feel angry—and helpless—just to think about it, and he was venting his anger on the patient causing her worry. 'With this storm, sending him anywhere's impossible. Don't worry about him,' he growled. 'Damned mainlander. He looks as strong as a horse.'

'He was unconscious for too long, Grandpa. I know his vital signs are OK, but if he has an intracranial bleed building... I want a scan.'

'Well, you won't get a scan on Briman Island.' The old doctor snorted. They were lucky to have simple X-ray facilities here and, heaven knew, he'd fought long and hard

enough to get those. 'Christie, his pupils are fine, his re
actions are OK and there's no sign of a skull fracture. H
got one lousy head knock and swallowed too much water
but I've seen many a fisherman with injuries worse tha
his live to tell the tale. And you say he's sensible now.'

'Well, almost sensible.' Christie couldn't stop a trace o
colour creeping into her face. 'If you call asking me t
marry him two minutes after he regained consciousnes
sensible.'

Stan chuckled. 'It sounds entirely sensible to me. I'd d
it myself if I were forty years younger and I wasn't you
grandpa.'

'And you weren't biased? I don't think so.' Christi
grinned, then sighed and ran her fingers through her mas
of unruly curls. She felt strange. It must be fatigue, sh
thought. There'd been no sleep last night. She'd been cop
ing with young Mary Adams's asthma attack and Li
Myers's threatened premature labour when the call ha
come through at about midnight that someone was in th
water in the harbour.

Luckily she'd had Mary's asthma settled and Liz's la
bour pains had eased. There'd been a crazy drive down t
the harbour with Ben's father in the driver's seat almos
mad with fear.

'They said Ben just dived straight in. They can't fin
him. God help me, Christie, if anything happens to tha
kid...'

The harbour-master had been out by then, alerted by th
other kids who'd been with Ben, and almost every able
bodied man on the island had been called to help. A flotill
of fishing boats had joined the search, risking darkness an
appalling weather to search for one of their own.

'They wouldn't have searched outside the harbour wal
if it hadn't been for young Ben,' Stan growled, watchin
her face. He'd caught up on what had happened by now

and was appalled by it. 'The fishermen took some huge risks—and you did, too, going out with them.'

'Mmm. I know.' The horror of the search would stay with Christie for a long time. Ben had been washed out through the harbour mouth, and the boy had spent almost an hour treading water in the open sea, fighting for breath and clinging to his unconscious burden as though his own life had depended on it.

It had been a miracle they'd found him, and it was a miracle they were both still alive.

'The boy must've been a mess,' Stan probed, and Christie nodded.

'He was.' She'd been well and truly seasick herself by then in her lookout position on the harbour-master's boat, but she'd forgotten everything else once the two bodies had been dragged into the boat.

Ben had been hysterical. Exhausted beyond belief, he'd collapsed sobbing and shaking on the deck. His father had held him and sworn over and over again while Christie had tried to revive the man he'd just rescued.

'He mustn't die. Don't let him,' Ben had sobbed as Christie had put everything she knew and a bit more into CPR. 'Doc, don't let him…'

'It would have hit him doubly hard after what happened to his mother,' Stan said softly, and Christie nodded.

Ben's mother had drowned when Ben was eight years old and the memories were still there, rising to haunt him. But there'd been little she could do for Ben last night.

'I couldn't help him much,' she said wearily.

'Dave said this chap's heart stopped?' Dave was the local harbour-master who'd co-ordinated the search.

'It did.' He must have stopped breathing just as they'd hauled him into the boat. Christie had put every ounce of strength and skill she possessed into resuscitation, while

Ben had sobbed and shaken and looked on with eyes that had expected death.

But then the stranger had coughed and spluttered and fought his way back to life, and in the next ward Ben could still hardly believe the miracle. But still he shook. The sedative Christie had administered was barely reaching him.

Stan could see the worry on his granddaughter's face. 'You should have woken me,' he growled. 'Hell, girl...'

'I was fine.' In truth, she hadn't been fine at all, but since her grandfather's stroke she'd diverted the house phone to her mobile. Nights for the old doctor were for sleeping now. Nothing else.

'So who is he?' she asked wearily. 'Do we know?'

'You didn't ask?'

'He's barely conscious,' she said. 'He needs to sleep. I figured it can wait.'

'Well, I can tell you his name,' Stan told her. He was obviously annoyed that he'd missed the drama of last night and his frustration showed. 'His boat's called *Sandpiper*. Dave's just phoned with information. He's been on to the authorities in Cairns. The boat's registered to a Charles Tallent, but it's logged as being skippered by his son, Hugo. He left Cairns on Thursday, heading to Brisbane. He should've taken cover in the Whitsundays when this storm blew up—heaven knows why he didn't.'

'I guess he's regretting it now.' Christie grimaced. 'So...it's Hugo Tallent.' She thought back to the man she'd just left. The name suited him, she thought. He was a big man, reaching the end of the bed with his bare feet, which would make him over six feet tall, and he looked as if he was in his mid thirties. Tanned, with a mop of unruly jet black curls, he was sun-weathered and strongly built. He was all brawn and no brain, she guessed, or why would he have put the boat at the harbour mouth on such a night? Good looks or not, he must be a fool!

So…why had the feel of his hand, the sight of his gorgeous body and the look of admiration in his pain-filled eyes made her insides do back flips?

The sensations came to her out of left field, totally unexpected and confusing. Which was bizarre! Dr Christie Flemming didn't think like that. She didn't have time for such nonsense.

So concentrate on other things, she told herself fiercely. Practicalities. 'Did Dave say what's happened to his boat? I guess he'll want to know.'

'He's managed to get it beached,' Stan told her. 'Seems it finally righted itself. It's lost its mast—Dave reckons that's maybe why he tried to run for cover in the harbour. It was thumping itself to bits on the harbour wall. They dragged it off and it's now up in dry dock. There's a heck of a lot of damage, but it's salvageable.'

'Our Mr Tallent's luckier and luckier,' Christie said dryly. She sighed. 'So all we need to do is patch him up and send him on his way—and then try and cope with the damage he's done to young Ben.'

'Our Ben's a hero,' Stan growled, and Christie shook her head.

'He might be, but he's a hero with scars. Last night will have opened a Pandora's box for him. I just hope to heaven we can close the lid again.'

It was three that afternoon before Christie found time to visit Hugo. He'd been specialled until then, which meant that he hadn't been left alone for a minute. She could hardly spare the nurses but, with the spectre of intracranial bleeds hanging over her, Christie was taking no chances. His vital signs had been checked over and over, and any slight change would have been reported instantly.

There had been no such worry—thankfully because she was busy enough and worried enough anyway—and by three o'clock she was feeling confident that the old doctor must have been right. The man must be OK.

He was asleep as she entered. Mary-anne stood up from her chair beside the bed and Christie motioned to the door.

'Hop it. He must be fine or he'd be showing symptoms by now. Have a coffee. I'll be here for ten minutes or so.'

Mary-anne gratefully hopped it. Christie lifted the clipboard from the foot of the bed, and Hugo opened his eyes.

They weren't half-bad as far as eyes went, Christie thought. They matched his gorgeous body exactly. Brown and deep set, they had laughter lines creasing in at the edges, as if he spent his life smiling. He might be a dimwit, she decided, but he must be a good-humoured dimwit.

She gave him a brief smile and went back to studying his report. The vomiting had stopped—he'd got rid of the sea water. He'd had a cup of tea for lunch but had eaten nothing. That was hardly surprising. Then he'd slept again.

No temperature, blood pressure fine. In fact...

'I'm normal?' he asked, and she started. His voice was low and deep. This morning it had been husky and shaken, but his confidence had returned.

'Nicely normal,' she said, and gave him a grin. 'As normal as someone with the IQ of a newt can ever be.' She lifted his wrist and checked her watch. 'Hmm.'

'I told you, I'm normal.'

'Let me listen to your chest.' She pulled his bedcover down and was presented with a broad expanse of tanned chest, liberally sprinkled with dark, curling hair. Goodness, the man could almost be one of those pin-up types—he-man material. She blinked, collected herself like a nicely trained female doctor should and attempted to adjust her stethoscope—and her thoughts—into professional mode.

'Can I ask—?'

'Hush,' she told him. 'I'm listening.'

Silence.

Then… 'Can I—?'

'Not yet. I'm still listening. Can you roll over onto your side?' she asked. 'Carefully, so you don't hurt your leg. I want to pop the stethoscope on your back.'

'Yes, ma'am.' There was enough dryness in his voice to make her blink, but he did what he was told. She listened—and frowned.

'What's wrong?' He rolled back onto his pillows to face her. She looked a little more professional now—her jeans were covered with a white coat—but she didn't look anything like the doctor Mary-anne had told him she was.

But he'd checked out his knee last time he'd woken. If it really had been dislocated—and it hurt like it had been—she'd put back a badly dislocated knee by herself, and that meant she had skill! Plus, Mary-anne had told him she'd resuscitated him. She might not have hauled him from the water but he still owed her his life.

'You're carrying a considerable amount of fluid on your lungs, which could cause a bit of discomfort,' she told him.

'I'll live.'

'Maybe you will, but I don't want you lying flat for a while,' she told him. 'You're to stay propped up on pillows for at least tonight. I don't want pneumonia.'

'That makes two of us,' he told her. His brows snapped together. 'I know you put my knee back, and Mary-anne tells me you resuscitated me when I was near dead, but…are you sure you're a doctor?'

She smiled at that. He wasn't the first person to question her credentials. 'Would you like to see my certificates?' she asked. 'I know I look sixteen but I'm twenty-eight and I have all the qualifications you could possibly want.' Her weary eyes twinkled and he felt the same kick in his guts that he'd felt the first time he'd seen her. 'I wouldn't try things I'm not competent to do,' she assured him, and he had the grace to give a shamefaced grin.

'Maybe it doesn't always follow. I wasn't exactly competent to try to come into the harbour. I gather I've risked a few lives, apart from my own stupid neck.'

'Mary-anne has been talking?' Mary-anne's husband was a local fisherman who'd been out last night in the search, and Mary-anne was nothing if not a straight talker. And it was true, it hadn't just been Ben who'd risked his life. It had been every islander who'd climbed onto a boat to search.

'Mary-anne has been talking,' he agreed dryly. 'It seems half the island put their lives on the line to save my butt.'

'Ben risked his life to save you,' she said softly. 'The islanders risked their lives to save *Ben*. He's quite a boy.'

He fell silent at that, while Christie checked his pupils and adjusted the drip above his bed.

'When can I see him?' he said at last, and his voice was strained. 'Ben, I mean.'

'I'm not sure.'

'You said he wasn't badly injured.'

'No, but...' Christie's voice faltered. 'He's not ready for visitors.'

Hugo's black eyebrows snapped together. 'Dr Flemming—you are Dr Flemming, I gather. The nurse told me...'

'Yes, I'm Dr Flemming.' She smiled at him. 'And you're Hugo Tallent.'

'Fine detective work.' His mind wasn't on her, though. 'Dr Flemming, you're not telling me everything.'

'About?'

'About Ben. Is he more badly injured than you've let on?'

'No.' She hesitated, wondering just how much she should say. It was Ben's business, and for all the brains he'd shown this man might be as sensitive as a Brahman bull.

But he'd need to see Ben before he left the island—most people in Hugo's position would insist on it, she thought—so if he wasn't to do more harm, then he probably needed to know the full story.

'Ben's mother drowned when he was eight,' she told him. There was no gentle way to put this. 'Ben was washed out in a rip, holding onto his surfboard. His mother panicked and swam out to reach him. She was lost, but they found Ben hours later, floating beyond the waves. I… He's carried it hard—that she died because of him.'

She hesitated but it had to be said. 'I think most of the reason you're here now is because of Ben's sheer, bloody-minded determination to save you, and that is a legacy from his past.'

'I see.'

'And you're not his mother,' she said softly, watching his face for signs of comprehension. 'No matter how much he'd want it to be. If you understand what I mean.'

He did. She could see it in the look of dismay and intelligent comprehension that flashed into his eyes as she spoke. And the consternation. Maybe she had to rethink this a little, then. He wasn't entirely a dope.

'Hell.'

'It is,' she said quietly. 'For Ben, it is. But meanwhile—'

'I *need* to see him.' It was a desperate growl and it made her blink.

'Maybe tomorrow,' she agreed. 'We'll get you a wheel-chair. I'm afraid you might not be weight-bearing on that knee for a day or two. It depends on the extent of the bruising. Meanwhile, if you're up to it, our local police sergeant would like to see you.'

'The police…'

'The sergeant needs to know what happened. Who to contact. I've held him off until now, but if you're up to it…'

'I'm up to it.' His mind clearly wasn't on his own problems. It was still on the boy. 'So much harm...' He flicked a look up at her. 'The islanders must think I'm a fool.'

'It has entered their minds,' she agreed neutrally, softening it with a smile. It wasn't her job to make him feel bad. He was doing a good enough job of that himself. 'But, then, we're inclined to think that of all mainlanders.' She glanced at her watch, but before she could leave, his hand came out and caught hers, holding her urgently to him.

'Please— I need to explain.'

She looked down at their linked hands. For heaven's sake, she had so much to do. She should pull away, but...

She gave an inward sigh, and capitulated, and there was a small part of her that was pleased she could do it. She sort of liked the feel of his hand...

'So, tell me,' she said, with more brusqueness than she intended. 'I'm listening.'

'Really?'

She smiled, disengaged her hand from his and sat on the chair beside him. It felt great to get the weight off her feet—and also, for some strange reason, it felt great to get her face on eye level with his. It lessened the doctor-patient relationship. It made her feel she was able to empathise just a little more, which, for some strange reason, felt really important.

And he seemed to feel it, too. He was watching her face, as if he badly wanted her to understand.

'It wasn't my boat,' he told her.

'No.'

'You know that already?' Still the tension was in his voice. He sounded as if he was close to breaking, and he needed to tell someone why. He needed to justify what was close to unjustifiable.

Christie sighed inwardly. Of course. What male didn't need to justify his foolhardiness? But if it helped, then she was ready to hear it. After all, it was better to listen than to prescribe a sedative. 'The harbour-master told me the boat's registered to your father,' she said gently.

'Yeah.' He looked grim. 'But my brother, Peter, borrowed it.'

'I don't understand.'

'Who does when Peter's concerned?' he said bitterly. 'My father lives in Brisbane. When he retired, he and my mother built the yacht and they loved it. Since my mother died it's been my father's life. I don't know how Peter managed to persuade him to lend it to him, but he did. Peter sailed it to Cairns, but then he was offered a berth on a bigger boat heading for the Bahamas. So Peter, being Peter, took off and left *Sandpiper* sitting in Cairns harbour. Not even in a safe berth.'

'So…'

'So my father decided to sail it home himself—but he has a dicky heart. It wasn't safe for him to try. It's the beginning of the cyclone season. If the boat doesn't get south now it'll be stuck in Cairns for six months, and six months without his boat would break my father more than anything else. And it's too big to haul by road.'

He hesitated, watching Christie closely and willing her to understand. For some reason, it was desperately important that she did. 'My father's just lost my mother,' he told her. 'He…he needs that boat.'

She softened, just a little. Maybe he wasn't a complete sandwich short of a picnic, then. 'I start to see.'

'I tried to hire someone to sail it south but had no takers,' he went on urgently. 'With my father more and more distressed, and saying he'd sail it himself, I had no choice. You might have gathered by now that I'm a fair-weather sailor. My radio failed, the storm hit from nowhere, I was dismasted and there was a lee shore. I was being driven onto the rocks. And without a radio…'

'It's rare for radios to fail.' Christie frowned. She knew enough of sailing to know that a decent radio was a sailor's lifeline.

Hugo's voice tightened in anger. 'That's courtesy of Peter,' he told her. 'He'd sold the good radio and replaced it with a cheap, battery-operated one—with no spare batteries—just like he sold every decent fitting to give him funds for his overseas jaunt. I refitted as best I could, but I was in a rush and a spare battery for the radio didn't occur to me.' He shrugged. 'So I sailed, I got into a mess and I checked Peter's notes, which said Briman Island is a safe harbour.'

'Which it is,' Christie told him. 'Once you're inside the harbour, it's fine, but it's not a safe harbour entrance. With an easterly blowing like it is now, not even the fishing boats can get in or out.'

'Except when they're taking hair-raising risks to save me.' Hugo groaned and sank back deep into the pillows. 'Of all the stupid, senseless, dopey…'

'Your boat's been salvaged,' Christie offered. She was so rushed for time that to sit here was stupid, but at least it was giving her the assessment she needed. The mental acuity test she could have been using after a period of unconsciousness—asking him questions like when he was born, what year it was now, who the current prime minister was—wasn't necessary while she did this. He'd been unconscious, but he didn't appear to have any brain injury at all.

The relief was enormous and she found her tense body relaxing as he spoke. He really was OK. Thank God! Drilling burr holes to relieve the pressure of an intracranial bleed wasn't an area of medicine that interested her one bit. Especially since she was on her own.

As well as that, it was sort of peaceful, talking to him. He was distressed, but there was an air of calm and competence about him. She couldn't put her finger on what it was exactly. Tranquillity, maybe? It was a ridiculous idea, but this was still blessed time out from what was waiting for her elsewhere in the hospital.

The tranquillity had to end. She had a major worry apart from her concerns over this man's head injury, Ben's horrors and her normal medical work. She'd spent the first part of last night worrying about Liz Myers's labour contractions. They'd eased but hadn't quite ceased. They must!

But Hugo Tallent wasn't thinking about her medical worries. He was thinking of what she'd just told him. 'The boat's been salvaged?' he repeated, staring at her like he couldn't believe what she'd said. '*Sandpiper* has been salvaged? You're kidding. I thought she was lost, for sure.'

Boat. *Sandpiper*.

Right. This man's boat was the least of her problems, but she could give him news that would leave one of them feeling better.

'I gather she righted herself, and was washed in through the harbour mouth,' she told him. 'It was incredibly lucky. She was washed up on the rocks of the harbour wall. The fishermen and the harbour-master have pulled her up into dry dock and they tell me she's repairable. With enough money.'

'Money's no problem.' He let his breath out in a sigh of relief. 'At least I can tell Dad she's safe, and he'll love repairing her.'

'He might have been more upset if his son had killed himself,' she said dryly. 'You'll need to let him know what's happened. Mary-anne will organise a phone by your bed.'

'I guess...' He hesitated. 'I'll need to charter a boat or light plane to get me off the island.'

'You don't like our medical facilities?' She smiled, but

there was strain around her eyes. Her other problems were crowding in, and he had no choice about staying.

'It's not that,' he said shortly. He stared down at the cradle over his injured leg. 'This leg is inconvenient, but I need to be back in Brisbane.'

'I'm more worried about your lungs than your leg,' she told him. 'But you're lucky. We have a retired physiotherapist living on the island. I've asked him to see if he can shift a bit of that fluid. It'll make you more comfortable.'

'I'll live,' he said shortly. 'There are physios in Brisbane. I can't stay here.'

That's what he thought. 'I'm sorry,' she said. 'But I'm afraid you're stuck with us for a bit. The weather's lousy. A cyclone's sweeping the north of the state and we're feeling it here. It's earlier than usual but that's what caused your problems. All emergency services are headed north, we can't land light planes and our harbour's unusable. So, unless you wish us to risk more lives on your behalf, Mr Tallent, I suggest you lie back and accept our hospitality.'

'But—'

'You may have money...' she told him, her gentleness fading. She was pushed to the limit and the last thing she needed was a rich, foolhardy yachtsman throwing his weight around. 'But I'm afraid money's no use to you here. Now, if you'll excuse me, I have work to do.'

She looked around as Mary-anne opened the door. Great. 'Can you take over, please, Nurse?' She spoke more formally than normal—in truth, her weariness was causing an edge she didn't normally feel. 'We can stop the specialling—just cut it back to hourly obs. I'll stop back in after the physio's been.'

'You're needed in the women's ward, Doctor,' Mary-anne said apologetically. 'Mrs Myers... Her contractions have started again. Strongly this time.'

Oh, help...

Christie closed her eyes for one weary moment. It was all the respite available for her, and it wasn't enough. Opening her eyes again, her face set into a grim mask.

'I'll leave you in Mary-anne's hands, then, Mr Tallent,' she said tightly. 'Get some rest.'

She closed the door behind her, leaving the yachtsman to take on board all that she'd told him.

And he didn't like any of it.

CHAPTER TWO

CHRISTIE had no more time to think of Hugo Tallent, or anyone else. Liz Myers was in real trouble.

Since Stan had had his stroke, babies weren't delivered on Briman Island—not if they had any sense. Their mothers went to the mainland a few weeks before delivery and stayed there until confinement. Although Christie had obstetric and surgical training, there were severe limits to what she could do alone.

Until the last few months she'd been able to cope in emergencies. Stan Flemming had been a fine doctor, and he and Christie worked well as a team. In the three years before Stan's stroke they'd operated as surgeon and anaesthetist for quick, straightforward procedures like emergency Caesareans.

But no more. Stan had lost sensation down his right side and was still slightly confused. Sometimes he seemed fine, but spasmodically he'd lose track of where he was or what he was doing, or he'd hold something and suddenly find it was on the floor. It meant that medically Christie was very much alone. It also meant the bright, confident smile she assumed as she entered the room where Liz Myers lay was totally false. Inside she was wobbling like jelly.

'Hi, Liz. What's happening?' Liz Myers was thirty-five weeks pregnant, but she was tiny and the baby was already big. On Christie's orders she'd gone to Townsville a month ago for a ultrasound and they hadn't liked what they'd found.

'Come back here no later than thirty-six weeks into your

24

pregnancy,' the Townsville obstetrician had told her. 'You're heading for a Caesarean.'

And on seeing the pictures from the ultrasound, Christie had agreed entirely. 'If you must marry a six-foot-six fisherman, with shoulders like an ox, then what do you expect?' she'd told her friend. 'Liz, you're tiny, Henry is a very big man and you're carrying Henry's son. You'll go back to Townsville.'

But they'd left it too late. Now Liz was lying pale and frightened and tiny, her giant of a husband was wringing his hands in fear and both were looking to her as if she could produce a miracle. She must!

'Can you do a Caesarean here?' Henry demanded as she entered the room. 'The Townsville doctors said she'll never deliver normally. Christie, you must be able to do a Caesarean…'

'Let's see what's happening first,' she told them, her heart sinking. She'd set up a Ventalin drip last night, which had seemed to have stopped Liz's early contractions, but now… One look as she lifted the sheet over Liz's tummy told her that these contractions weren't intending to stop.

Christie thought back to the scans the Townsville obstetrician had sent her. 'The baby's head is almost bigger than the pelvic span at thirty weeks,' he'd written bluntly. 'There's no way he's coming out the way God meant him to. I'd like her to stay in Townsville now, but she refuses. Make sure she's well back here by thirty-six weeks.'

Liz was still only thirty-five weeks but the baby had ideas of his own as to when he was due. Like now!

Help…

She checked the CTG and her heart sank further. The baby's heart rate was fluctuating from 130 down to 100, with a slow recovery phase. Double help…

'Do you want me to fetch Dr Stan?' Louise asked as Christie timed the contractions. Louise was the island's most junior nurse, but even she knew that what was happening here spelled serious trouble. The contractions were two minutes apart and quickening.

'No.' What could her grandfather do except feel angry about his helplessness?

But what could she do alone? Why on earth had she chosen to practise medicine in such an isolated place?

At medical school her friends had mocked her. 'You'll do nothing but stitch up fishing accidents and call in the air ambulance to evacuate patients,' they'd told her.

But they hadn't understood Briman Island's pull. A child of brilliant but distant parents, Christie had spent every holiday she could here with her doctor grandparents and she'd known how much the islanders had loved their Dr Stan and Dr Martha. They'd needed them, and for forty years her grandparents had coped with depression, snakebite, fevers... Everything.

Her grandparents had loved the island, and so had Christie, so when Grandma Martha—or Doc Martha as the islanders had called her—had died, Christie hadn't hesitated to take her place. After all, Grandpa was just seventy, she'd thought, so they could be partners. He couldn't work alone.

As she couldn't now. Grandpa's stroke had robbed her of her helpmate, and no one else would come. To practise in such an isolated place... 'You'd have to be mad,' her friends had said, and right at this minute Christie was inclined to agree.

Dear heaven...

With the foetal heartbeat dipping to a hundred, this baby was obviously in the early stages of distress. He wasn't too bad yet, the heartbeat was strong enough, but if she waited any longer...

This baby wasn't waiting until the weather cleared—if she waited any longer and there were further signs of foetal distress she'd be in even worse trouble. To perform a

Caesar and then have a flat or distressed baby at the end of it...

She'd have to do a Caesar, but to do it alone...

She thought it through, trying to figure out how the Caesars she'd performed in the past could have been done with one doctor.

Could they?

She'd have to use a general anaesthetic. She was fighting panic and forcing her frightened mind to think. An epidural was what was best for the patient—especially for a premature baby—but she couldn't manage a conscious patient, an epidural anaesthetic, the huge incision a Caesarean needed, plus a newborn baby.

She could hardly cope with it under general anaesthetic—but at least if she gave the initial anaesthetic, maybe they could rig up a mainland phone link so an anaesthetist could talk Mary-anne through the rest of the procedure while she herself operated. Could Grandpa do it?

No, she thought. It might work, but if he got confused halfway through and gave Mary-anne the wrong instructions or the wrong dosage— No!

And if the baby needed help?

It didn't bear thinking of. All her attention would need to be on Liz. She could hardly stop bleeding and resuscitate a newborn babe at the same time.

What was the alternative? There wasn't any, she decided bleakly. This baby wasn't planning on waiting until the weather cleared and they could get a plane to land. The forecasters were saying two days of high winds. Two days...

She did a vaginal check, and grimaced. The obstetrician had been right. Liz's pelvis was so small...

The baby hadn't started moving down yet. That was one thing at least. Liz was hardly dilated at all and the baby was still OK. There was no frantic rush, but if she had to

operate then she preferred to operate now, before there wa
one. If the baby's heart rate faltered there'd be no time t
set up the phone links.

'Get Mary-anne from Mr Tallent's room,' she tol
Louise. At least Mary-anne was a midwife. Even traine
nurses were thin on the ground on this island. 'Tell her
need her now. Everything else can wait. You go back ont
ward work. Keep up the obs on Mr Tallent, and Mary-ann
and I will take over here.' She needed two more nurses a
least, but Mary and Ben still needed attention in the kids
ward and she couldn't conjure nurses out of thin air.

She turned to Liz, took her hand and steadied her ow
racing heart. She needed to be calm, confident and reas
suring to these people—which was the last thing she felt
but needs must. 'Liz, you realise we need to do
Caesarean. Your little one wants to make it into the world
and he won't wait for the weather to clear!'

'But…' Liz faltered. 'Can you do it on your own?'

'Mary-anne's a trained midwife,' Christie told her, stil
holding onto that smile of reassurance which was a tota
lie. 'So there's no problem. Just lie back and think abou
baby names.'

'But…' Liz had obviously been doing pre-natal reading
'You can do it with an epidural?'

'I'm afraid I can't,' Christie told her. 'We'll do it unde
a general.'

'Oh, no!' It was a terrified whisper.

'It'll be fine,' Christie said strongly, much more strongl
than she felt. Please, God…

It took a while for Mary-anne to arrive. There must prob
lems elsewhere in the hospital, Christie figured as she mad
her preparations. Mary-anne knew the need was urgent.

Great! That was all she needed. Both nurses were gon
for far too long. Something must have delayed them.

Please, don't let Hugo Tallent's headache be getting worse. A vision of two patients on two operating tables flicked into her exhausted mind, and the vision almost overwhelmed her.

She blocked it. She couldn't investigate. There was no time, and triage told her this was her priority. There were two lives at risk here—Liz's and her baby's.

Forcing herself to keep steady and measured, she explained the procedure she intended to use to a terrified Liz and Henry. She sorted her equipment, she set up the humidicrib so it would be warm to receive the baby, and was sorting drugs when the ward door swung open. Thank heaven…

It wasn't just Mary-anne, though. It was Mary-anne following a wheelchair, and the wheelchair held Hugo Tallent!

Why on earth was he here?

Hugo was dressed—sort of—in a green hospital gown. His leg was out on a support in front of him, a drip stand was attached to the back of the chair and he looked every inch an invalid. Except for his expression. His face held the look of a man who wasn't letting anything stand in his way. Christie's gaze turned to Mary-anne, and Mary-anne looked as stunned as she was.

'I couldn't stop him,' the nurse said helplessly. She was holding the handles of his wheelchair but Hugo had been propelling himself. 'He said he needs to see you.'

Christie took a deep breath. Great! This was all she needed—a nut case as a patient.

'Mr Tallent, I'm busy,' she told him brusquely, pushing her stray curls back from her forehead and trying not to lose focus. She had so much to concentrate on that she felt dizzy! Somehow, though, she made her voice as stern as she could—doctor supremely unimpressed by recalcitrant patient! 'This is a private ward, and Mrs Myers is having a baby. Could you, please, return to your room? *Now!*'

'Mary-anne says you're attempting a Caesarean on your own.' He was intent on his own line of thought, and his voice was flat and incisive.

'Yes, but what—?'

'You can't do it.'

'Of course I can,' she said bluntly. The last thing she wanted was someone voicing her own uncertainties. 'Mary-anne's a trained midwife and—'

'You need an anaesthetist.'

'I don't have one,' she snapped. 'This is none of your business. Will you get back to bed?'

'You do have one,' he told her, his eyes resting on hers. Despite the incongruity of his appearance, his look was steady, sure and strong, telling her that he spoke the absolute truth. 'And, no, I won't go back to bed. I'm a qualified anaesthetist and I'm here to help.'

Silence.

More silence and more silence still. It was all Christie could do to breathe.

An anaesthetist! She had an anaesthetist right here!

Right up to that moment she hadn't realised how scared she'd been. She put out a hand and held onto the bed, and suddenly she needed that support to stop herself falling. Her weariness was almost overwhelming.

'You're an *anaesthetist?*' she managed, and her voice actually squeaked.

'Yes.'

'But you're a—'

'Dope?' He smiled, his dark eyes creasing into laughter. 'Agreed. But just because I'm a dope as a sailor, it doesn't make me a dope as an anaesthetist.' He looked over at the woman on the bed and, despite his ridiculous dress and invalid appearance, his eyes were warm and infinitely reassuring. It seemed he guessed the young mother's terror.

'I qualified as a doctor fifteen years ago,' he told Liz,

nd there may as well not have been any other person in
he room. 'I've been working as an anaesthetist at Royal
South Hospital in Brisbane for the last five years. If you or
your husband contact my hospital they'll give you all the
professional references you need. Hey—just imagine I'm
on temporary loan from the city. Believe it or not, I'm
extremely competent.'

He looked down at his hospital gown and grinned. 'They
say appearance maketh the man, but it's not always true.
I'm very good at giving anaesthetics for Caesareans. I can
practically do it with my eyes closed. So how about it,
ma'am? Will you let a one-legged, undressed, half-drowned
sailor give you an anaesthetic?'

Christie stared. So did Liz. As Liz's eyes widened, so
did Hugo's smile. He was still totally focussed on Liz. The
most important thing at the moment was to allay her terror,
and he knew it.

'I promise you that I'm competent and fit enough to operate,' he told Liz, still intent on reassurance. 'I know I've
just been spectacularly soaked. I have a sore knee and a
headache, but for the benefit of Dr Flemming, who I'll bet
is not exactly aching to drill burr holes after she's performed a single-handed Caesarean, if I had major damage
my headache would be worse by now—not fading, as it is.
So I'm fine.' Then, with a sideways smile at Christie—he
was reassuring her as well as Liz, Christie realised—he
added a rider to Liz and her husband.

'Dr Flemming is capable of giving you the anaesthetic—
I have no doubt of that—but, working alone, she'll need to
put you to sleep. She'll give you a general anaesthetic. Also
she'll have no one to help when the baby's born. I can give
you an epidural so you can watch your little one arrive in
the world, and I can be there to assist the baby if there's a
need.'

'But…' Liz sounded almost as befuddled as Christie. She

was clutching her husband's hand. Another contraction had just passed and she was no longer in control, but she needed to be sure. 'You don't look like a doctor.'

'I don't.' Hugo flashed another of those magnetic grins. 'But, to be fair, neither does Dr Flemming. At least I don't have freckles and I look more than twelve! I'll admit that in this hospital gown I'm even less respectable from behind than from the front, but you need to ignore appearance here. Concentrate on what's important.'

Then he reached to take Liz's hand, and in that touch Christie knew that he surely was a doctor. With that one touch—and from the look in his eyes—she knew that Hugo had stood at patients' bedsides a thousand times, and he'd dispensed comfort and reassurance wherever he'd been.

And somehow, despite his appearance—despite the fact that he looked as if he was about to be operated on rather than operate himself—she knew instinctively that he was all that he'd said he was. And inexplicably she knew that he was good.

'Trust me,' he said softly to Liz. 'Yes?'

'Y-yes,' she said, her voice wavering. She looked at Christie. 'I... Will you get my baby out?'

'Of course we will,' Christie told her. There was nothing else to say. 'There are no problems here, Liz. We'll take you into Theatre straight away and introduce ourselves to your impatient son.'

It went like clockwork.

Christie could hardly believe it. After all her fears...

They adjusted the operating table to make it as low as possible so Hugo could stay in his wheelchair. It was lucky that Christie was short and Hugo was tall—they could cope okay.

Whatever—Christie was no longer solely in charge. As they worked, organising equipment, setting up the table and scrubbing, Christie tried to fill Hugo in on Liz's background, but when they returned to the table Hugo fired off his own swift questions at Liz. Background. General health. Allergies.

He was double-checking her work, Christie thought with weeping relief. She'd do that herself if she were him. Double-check all the time…

'Have you given steroids?' he asked.

'Yes,' she told him, flushing. 'Dexamethasone. I gave it yesterday at the first sign of labour.'

'Great.' And he gave her an assessing stare—the kind she'd had in the past. Anaesthetist wondering just what sort of surgeon he had here…

She didn't care, she thought dazedly. He could give her any kind of stare he wanted. He was the answer to her prayers!

Once started, for the first couple of moments she watched him, but it only took that time to be sure he knew his stuff. He handled the monitors as if born to them. She watched as he filled the first syringe, she listened to the orders he snapped at Mary-anne and finally she relaxed.

She returned to monitoring the baby and preparing her own equipment as he moved Liz onto her side and skilfully injected the epidural drugs into her spine.

If a medical council demanded why she'd let an unqualified doctor near her patient she'd have to defend this as a life-or-death decision, she thought, but this man couldn't be unqualified. He'd done this before, he'd done it recently and he'd done it well.

So all she had to do was concentrate on her part. To retrieve one baby.

The epidural was taking hold. As Christie set up a catheter, Hugo was touching Liz's skin, asking about sensations, watching her face. Her legs were numbing, and slowly the anaesthetic took hold over her abdomen.

'Can you feel this?' Hugo asked as he touched her swollen tummy, and she shook her head.

'Right.' He smiled at Christie. 'Nearly there. Over to you, Dr Flemming. Let's see what you can do.'

Mary-anne set up a sheet to block the incision sight from Liz and Henry, and Christie swiftly prepped Liz's swollen tummy. Her eyes flicked to Hugo's. He gave a swift nod and a reassuring smile—the area was completely numbed by now and she could move.

She took one last flickering glance at the screen showing the baby's heartbeat. It was dipping to ninety-five. This baby was as ready now as he ever would be to come into the world. He needed to be born.

She lifted the scalpel. Now Hugo was on his own—she had eyes only for what she was doing—but maybe he was more competent than she was.

She took a deep breath, but there was no room for indecision. She had to go in and she had to move fast. She looked up at Hugo, gave him a brief nod in return—and then moved. She made a long, sweeping, transverse incision, just as if she did this three times a day. Ha! She hadn't done one since she'd come to the island.

But her basic knowledge was sound. The procedures had been thoroughly instilled into her, and they came back as if by instinct. Thank God! She carefully mobilised the bladder downwards. The uterus lay exposed, stretched to the limit...

Mary-anne moved in with the sucker as Christie carefully cut the uterine membranes and the amniotic fluid gushed forth. Then the forceps magically landed in her hand. That was Hugo, acting as assistant as well as anaesthetist. He'd seen that she needed them but Mary-anne wasn't free. There was no time for acknowledgement.

Where...?

The tiny head was right where it was meant to be. It was

perfect normal presentation. Thanks be. There wasn't a itch.

Liz could feel nothing and even Henry was holding up ell. Christie had seen big men go down in dead faints as ıey'd watched their wives deliver, but Henry sensed—as ıey all did—that there was no room for nonsense here. He ıas talking Liz through what they were doing and she was ven answering him in soft murmurs while Christie man-euvred the forceps around the baby's head. There was no ossibility of Liz doing that if the epidural was the least awed.

It wasn't. There was no pain at all. Carefully, skilfully, 'hristie brought the baby forward, lifting its head clear and ıen scooping it out to lie it on his mum's tummy.

This was the crucial time. Heavens, the bleeding… The aby…

But Hugo was there. She wasn't alone. She could clear way the placenta and tend to the bleeding while Hugo lamped and cut the umbilical cord. She was dimly aware f him clearing the baby's airway as Mary-anne swabbed nd she started to suture the uterus. They were acting to-ether as one, each instinctively knowing what was needed.

Hugo was good, she thought gratefully. So good!

And then, magically, the thing was done. Within mo-ıents Hugo was placing one tiny, lusty baby boy into Iary-anne's waiting arms, ready for introductions to his arents.

And Christie didn't know who was more stunned, the aby, the parents—or her. But she was so grateful she was lose to tears. She'd left the baby totally to Hugo, but one ook at mother and baby was enough to know that all was vell.

How could it not be? The little one's yell of indignation vas enough to wake the dead!

'Well done,' Hugo said softly, and she flushed with plea
sure.

'Well done yourself,' she told him, but he shook hi
head.

'Anaesthetics is what I do, lady. That was one efficien
Ceasarean from a general practitioner.'

It shouldn't matter. Praise shouldn't make any differenc
at all, but it did. It made her feel fantastic. Top-of-the-worl
fantastic.

The baby was premature. He wasn't fully developed, an
the last thing he'd needed had been a general anaestheti
crossing the placenta into his tiny body. Plus, she'd hav
been able to give him no attention at all. She'd have run
real risk of losing him if she'd had to operate alone.

And now it was over. Mother and baby were safe, an
Christie's emotions were threatening to overwhelm her. Sh
sutured the wound with swift, sure stitches, trying to hol
back tears of happiness and relief and aware that Hugo'
eyes were on hers.

'You're exhausted,' he said softly, adjusting the salin
drip. 'I can cope with this,' he told her. 'There's no prob
lems with the baby and I'm quite capable of suturing. Leav
Mary-anne and me to finish up here.'

But that was taking things too far. She might have al
lowed an unknown doctor to give an anaesthetic in a
emergency, but to leave him in charge... And he *still* ha
a headache and he *still* had fluid on his lungs!

'Uh-uh.' She shook her head and bit her lip. 'Mary-anne
could you ask Louise to take Mr Tallent back to bed?'

'The label is ''Dr'' Tallent,' he said, his eyes creasin
into teasing laughter. 'Or don't you believe me yet?'

'I believe you.' Epidurals were one of the hardest an
aesthetics to get exactly right, and she knew now that thi
man was the best. 'But you're my patient and you're suf
fering from a head wound.'

'Still hankering after drilling burr holes?' he teased, and Christie flushed. He had her totally unsettled.

'No.' She bit her lip. 'But... Please, go back to bed.' In truth she was so weary and confused that she could hardly think. She needed time out.

He seemed to sense it. As Louise entered the room in response to the bell push, he looked at her and smiled again.

'Very well, Dr Flemming,' he said. 'Never let it be said that Dr Tallent doesn't know when he's not wanted. OK, troops.' He held up his hands in mock surrender. 'Wheel me away.'

If only someone would do that for her...

Christie finished Liz's suturing and checked the infant. She'd placed him in a humidicrib where he'd stay until she was sure everything was fine, but, apart from the fuzz of soft hair all over his body that told her he was premature, he looked terrific. If he'd gone to term he could well have been a twelve-pounder, she thought, wincing for Liz. As it was, he was a healthy seven.

'We've been very lucky,' she told Liz, and Liz gave her an exhausted smile.

'I know. Isn't he lovely?'

'He is, that.' Christie looked down at the tiny baby and gave a crooked smile, but to her surprise Liz was laughing at her.

'Not him, stupid,' she whispered. Liz Myers was a friend as well as a patient. She and Christie were the same age and had spent their childhood holidays exploring every inch of Briman Island together, plus getting into every conceivable type of scrape. Now, while her husband was away making very important phone calls, the new mother somehow found the energy to tease her friend. 'Of course our baby is gorgeous, but I meant our wonderful Dr Tallent.'

'Oh...'

Liz managed a chuckle.

'It seems you have a much more interesting patient than me,' she whispered. 'And you don't need to tell me—you *are* interested!'

Was she?

Christie headed back to the nurses' station, made herself a really strong coffee and sank back onto a chair in relief. It felt *so* good to stop for a moment—to have a moment's respite.

And Liz's comments drifted back.

Was she interested?

It was a stupid question, she decided. How could she be interested in a man she knew nothing about? Sure, he was an anaesthetist—a very competent and good-looking anaesthetist, she conceded—but he was a Brisbane specialist and that was all she knew. For all she knew he had a wife and three kids.

Maybe he was gay!

Gay? No!

She remembered the feel of his eyes on hers, and the random thought flew out the window. He was definitely not gay, she told herself firmly. No, no and *no!* Maybe he was a bit too much the other way for her liking.

She wrinkled her nose at where her thoughts were taking her. Ridiculous places! Places it wasn't worth the effort to think about. The one thing Dr Christie Flemming didn't have time for was a love life.

When Christie had made the decision to practise medicine on Briman Island she'd accepted that her chances of marriage were somewhere between zero and nothing. The islanders saw her as a doctor, and nothing more. If a local lad had fancied his chances, threatening to burden her with children and domestic responsibilities, the rest of the islanders would have come close to tarring, feathering and banishing him to the mainland!

It wasn't quite as obvious as that, Christie thought rue-
ally, but it was there for all that. Unsaid, but thought. The
landers left her strictly alone. The doctor was one apart—
ot like any other woman. Untouchable.

More than forty years ago, Doctors Martha and Stan had
ome to the island already married. Christie had come
lone, and that was how she'd stay.

'Which is fine by me,' Christie told herself wearily,
moving herself reluctantly to her feet again. 'Anyone
ouches me now and I'll fall right over. Dinner and a nap
efore evening rounds, Dr Flemming, or you'll drop where
ou stand.' The events of the night before—plus the decent
out of seasickness—had taken their toll and were threat-
ning to overwhelm her. 'Just head for the cottage and put
ourself to bed for an hour. And take it from there.'

he woke at seven the next morning.

Christie opened one eye and then the other. Then she
lanced at the clock on her bedside table, gave a yelp of
orror and sat bolt upright. She'd slept for thirteen hours
traight!

Thirteen hours! How…?

She was still wearing the jeans and sweater she'd lain
lown in last night, but the morning sun was streaming
hrough her bedroom window, the storm waves were crash-
ng on the beach, the sea was glistening in the morning
un—it had finally stopped raining—and the island's bird
opulation was declaring that it was indeed morning.

'Grandpa!' She flung her bedcovers back, yelling almost
as she woke. Dear heaven… She hadn't even checked on
he old man last night.

She always checked Stan, every four hours. His
reathing was so shaky. She worried about pneumonia, as
e kept turning onto his back in his sleep and shoving away
is pillows.

She'd set her alarm. What had happened?

The hospital must have rung for orders. Why hadn't she heard the phone? She should have checked Liz and her baby again, and Hugo Tallent, and Mary Adams, and Ben...

First things first. 'Grandpa!'

He wasn't in his room!

'Grandpa!'

No answer. She dived for the front door, flung it open—and her grandfather was coming up the beach path to the house. He was walking carefully on his frame, and beside him, looking dapper and dressed and ready for the day, was Hugo Tallent.

Christie's home was one of a pair of whitewashed fisherman's cottages about five hundred yards from the hospital. Christie usually drove Stan to and from the hospital but now he was operating under his own steam. As was Hugo.

Hugo was in his wheelchair but he was pushing himself, his strong hands easily propelling the wheels. It was hard for him to slow to the old man's pace, Christie saw, but he did it carefully, matching her grandfather exactly.

Grandpa saw her as she opened the door, and he grinned and waved. The pair of them looked absurdly pleased with themselves.

'Good morning, lass,' Stan called. 'Had a good sleep?'

Hugo grinned, too. 'Top of the morning to you, Dr Flemming, and it's a wonderful morning—if only this wind would die. I'm thinking of getting my chair fitted with sails. I'd be halfway across the island by now.'

She had no answer. She was so dazed she didn't know what to say. Instead, she stood back and watched as the odd couple manoeuvred themselves through the door.

They didn't manage it without difficulty. Stan always had trouble, but Christie knew better than to try and help. This was an ancient fisherman's cottage with stone walls two feet thick. The doors weren't built for walking frames—or for wheelchairs—and Hugo had to manoeuvre back and forth until he finally made it.

'Your grandpa asked me for breakfast,' Hugo told her. She was still stunned as Stan made a beeline for the kettle and his beloved cuppa, but Hugo seemed every inch at home. He filled the kitchen with his presence. 'Stan's promised me wood-fired toast, island butter and home-made strawberry jam. Is that OK with you, Dr Flemming?'

'I… Fine. It's Grandpa's house.' Christie put a dazed hand up to her riot of curls and pushed them out of her eyes—hoping maybe he'd look different if she did. He didn't. 'I guess…'

'You look ruffled,' Hugo said kindly. 'Doesn't she look ruffled, sir?' He turned to Stan. 'Do you think we're upsetting her by barging in like this?'

'She looks like she slept in her clothes more like,' Stan growled. 'Like she does half her life. These days she sleeps on the run. Go and have a shower, lass, and come and eat with us.'

'But…' She looked helplessly from Stan to Hugo and back again. 'I need to check… The hospital…'

'The hospital is fine,' Stan told her. 'Hugo and I have seen to everything.'

Hugo and I…

'What exactly have you seen to?' she asked, her heart sinking. Stan was liable to get confused. If he'd measured drugs, or ordered dosage changes, or tried to set up a drip…

'Don't look so worried,' Stan told her. Normally he'd hate this type of inquisition. He knew he couldn't cope, but it broke his heart that he couldn't. Now, though, he parried her worry with good humour. 'When you had your nap last night this young fella and I had a talk. I knew you were dead beat, and we could help each other. So after he finished having his chest pounded—his lungs are clear now, by the way—we organised a system.'

'A system...'

'First we shot Louise over to turn off your alarm,' he told her, his enjoyment increasing as the look of astonishment on her face grew. 'It was only sensible,' he went on. 'You'd gone thirty six hours without sleep and it was crazy to go longer.'

'But...'

'Then Hugo and I did a ward round,' he continued. 'I introduced him to everyone, we went over charts together, discussed medication, did what needed to be done...'

Christie's eyes flew to Hugo's. He gazed calmly back at her, his brown eyes tranquil. His eyes gave her a message, nonetheless. Nothing had been done that shouldn't have been done. Things were fine.

'Grandpa—'

But Stan was unstoppable. 'Then Hugo suggested I sleep in the ward last night so we could be woken together if things went wrong. Nothing did—apart from old Mrs Grayson's drip packing up which Hugo didn't bother to wake me for because his fingers are a darn sight steadier than mine.'

She shook her head, thinking this through. 'But Ben. I meant to spend time with him last night.'

'Hugo had a long talk to him last night,' Stan told her. 'The kid slept like a log. Same as you. Hugo's been with him again just now, and reckons he's fine. So you can take that worried look off your face, girl, and go and get yourself decent. For once in your life you have no work to do.'

No work to do!

Christie stood under the shower and let that sink in. She was still confused, but she was feeling light years younger than she'd felt the day before.

It hadn't just been the thirty-six hours without sleep which had left her exhausted, she thought dazedly, examining why she felt so different. It was the culmination of overwhelming work she'd faced since Stan's stroke, together with the burden of looking after Stan.

In one night Hugo had lifted that burden for thirteen glorious hours. She didn't know how he'd persuaded the old man to sleep at the hospital, but it had been a masterstroke. She knew without him telling her—there was something about the look of sheer intelligence in Hugo's brown eyes—that he'd seen the problem, and he'd had the nurses slip in and check on Stan as often as she did here. If Stan had slipped down on his pillows and had spent the night without breathing easily, he wouldn't have been as sprightly as he was this morning.

So now she'd had thirteen hours sleep without any dire consequences. She felt like she'd been handed a million dollars. No, better!

She towelled and dressed in clean T-shirt and jeans—in truth, she owned little else. Then she ran a comb through her damp curls and for some reason she stared at her reflection for just a moment longer than usual before she left her room. Her reflection looked puzzled. It was as if something was changing but she didn't know what.

As if *she* was changing.

Ridiculous. She gave herself a rueful grin and told herself she was imagining things.

Out in the kitchen the men were making toast on the wood stove. Hugo was holding a piece of bread to the flame on his toasting fork, and as Christie re-entered the kitchen the scene before her was so domestic that she blinked.

So did Hugo.

'Wow,' he said, his eyes creasing into a smile of welcome. Despite her lack of cosmetics, her damp curls and her bare toes, he thought she looked gorgeous. By the look

in his eyes there was no mistaking what he thought, and
Stan saw and chuckled.

'She's quite a lass, my Christie,' he said, and Hugo nodded.

'She is at that, sir. Not like most doctors in my circle o
aquaintances.'

'Cut it out, you two.' Christie tried to glower but it didn'
quite come off. Her cheeks were on fire. This man made
her feel strange, and she wasn't at all sure she liked the
sensation. 'Do I really not need to go to the hospital straigh
away?'

'Glenys is in charge and she'll ring the moment she
needs us,' Hugo told her.

She frowned. 'Glenys?'

'Glenys is your charge nurse,' he said kindly, and she
shot him a look of exasperation.

'*I* know who Glenys is. I'm just surprised *you* do.'

'Hey, I know everyone in the hospital,' he assured her
He motioned to the clothes he was wearing—a khaki fish
erman's jersey, moleskin trousers and yachties' shoes
'Mary-anne brought me in a pile of her husband's clothes
and stopped for long enough to give me a who's-who guide
to the whole island. If you need any local gossip, just ask
me.'

'But...'

'Toast?' he enquired. 'It's very good.'

'I do need to go,' she managed. 'Liz's baby—'

'Baby Myers is already drinking,' he said blandly. 'Liz
has expressed colostrum and he's taken a little—enough to
make everyone happy. I'm sure we can take him out of the
humidicrib for feeding but we left that decision for you.'

'As we did Hugo's leg.' Stan chortled. 'He's not too
happy about sitting in a wheelchair, but I reckoned I'd like
someone with twenty-twenty eyesight to have a look before
he bears weight. The agreement we made with each other

last night was that we wouldn't do a thing that both of us weren't happy with. So he had to stick with the wheelchair until you check it. Together we make one fine doctor, Christie, love.'

Together they did. Christie looked down at her grandpa, calmly sipping his tea, and she felt a lump the size of an orange form in her throat. Stan had been so unhappy—so humiliated by his illness—but in this one night Hugo had given him back his dignity. Stan had been able to help his granddaughter when she'd been in trouble, and that one small thing...

She grabbed a tissue from the sideboard and blew her nose—hard.

'You're not catching a cold, I hope?' Hugo asked. He was watching her thoughtfully, but there was a twinkle in his eyes that showed he knew exactly what she was thinking. And why she'd blown her nose.

'It's hay fever.' She sniffed. 'All this wind.'

'And all this hay,' he agreed, the twinkle deepening. He looked out of the window at sea, sand and seaweed. 'Yep, I can see it.'

'You know darn well hay fever is caused by more than hay.'

'I'm only an anaesthetist and failed sailor, lady,' he told her. 'What would I know?' He chuckled and pulled his toasting fork back from the fire to check his handiwork. 'But I do have a new skill. Toast-maker! Do try some of my cooking, Dr Flemming. I think you'll find it extraordinarily good.'

And she did.

Toast, in fact, had never tasted so good. Sitting at the kitchen table, her elbows spread on the scrubbed pine and her mouth full of hot buttered toast, Christie started to feel so good she felt almost unreal. Floating.

This man kept her in a bubble of laughter. He joked with

her grandfather but was deeply respectful of all the old man had to say. He asked intelligent questions, listened, made soft jokes that made the old man smile—in short, he brought a new lease of life to the kitchen which hadn't been there since her grandmother had died.

Christie drank it in, and so did her grandfather. This man was here for such a short while, Christie thought ruefully. She could afford to absorb it while she could. Their contact with the mainland was sparse—her medical contact almost negligible, apart from hearing back about patients she'd sent away for treatment.

And Hugo was a fine doctor. It stood out a mile. As they talked over the patients they had in the hospital, discussing their treatment, he made her feel as she had during training, as if medicine was wonderful and exciting and new and interesting. Not the hard slog she now knew it to be.

She ate four pieces of toast and drank three cups of coffee without thinking, and then suddenly realised it was nine o'clock. Reluctantly she rose to leave. It had to end some time. Surgery was at ten, and she had to do a round…

'But check my leg first,' Hugo said as she stacked away their dishes. 'I need to be out of this dratted wheelchair and your grandpa is threatening to chain me in without your clearance. I have things to do. I can't be staying here.'

'You can't leave the island,' she told him—a trifle too quickly—and he shook his head.

'No.' He smiled, and his eyes met here. 'Believe it or not, I'm growing more resigned by the minute.' Then, ignoring her flush, or maybe his smile deepened because of it, he turned back to Stan. 'I need to make arrangements for my father's boat. I did some telephoning last night and if it's OK with you, sir, and you, Christie, I'll stay on until Friday.'

Friday. It was only Monday now. Despite herself,

Christie couldn't stop a little frisson of pleasure building from within.

She pushed it down firmly. This was nonsense. What was the likes of her doing with such a thought? She was the island doctor, and the island doctor led a very straight and narrow life.

Allowing herself to be distracted would only lead to un-happiness. For everyone.

'That's…that's fine,' she managed. 'Isn't it, Grandpa?'

'Mary-anne says there's a bed-and-breakfast establishment on the other side of the island where I can stay,' he told them. 'I can't stay in the hospital.'

'You can stay here,' Stan declared before Christie could say a word. 'Can't he, Christie? We have a spare room.'

'That's very kind…'

'It's not kind in the least.' Grandpa was in charge, and he was enjoying himself. 'It's a commercial proposition. You can pay by making us toast every morning.' He chuckled. 'And by talking to us about life outside the island. Sometimes the pair of us go nuts with boredom.'

Did he? Christie flashed a concerned glance at her grandfather. He never said he was bored.

She was sometimes bored herself—unutterably bored. Or maybe not bored as much as lonely.

But not now. 'Well, thank you. It'd be a real pleasure,' Hugo was saying, his slow, lazy smile directed at Christie. 'I can't tell you how much. Hey, if I haul these trousers off, can you check my knee, Dr Flemming? And then you can take me off the invalid list.'

CHAPTER THREE

HUGO'S knee, as far as dislocated knees went, seemed fine. Christie's urge was to take him back up to the hospital and check it, but Hugo Tallent, having found himself invited to stay in their cottage, was intent on just that.

'Nope. I'm staying put. As far as hospitals go, I like being on the doctor's end of the stethoscope. If you show me my bedroom now, we'll go from there.'

It shouldn't have made any difference where she examined him, Christie thought crossly as she unbandaged his leg and checked the mass of bruising around his knee. This was just a *knee* for heaven's sake. It was only marginally attached to a man, and she was a doctor treating a *knee*.

So why the sight of Hugo lying back on his bed, wearing only his boxer shorts and his big fisherman's jersey, had the effect of unnerving her completely she didn't know.

And she didn't want to know, she thought breathlessly. His smile was growing by the minute. He guessed what she was thinking—and she couldn't begin to think in that direction.

But she was!

'What's the story?' He might have checked the knee himself but he seemed content to leave it to her, lying back on the pillows and wincing as she gently prodded the damaged ligaments. But still the laughter remained, and somehow she stayed in doctor mode. She lifted his foot and held his lower leg, moving it gently to the extent of its rotation and watching his face as she did.

There was nothing except general discomfort.

'You're not being exceptionally brave?' she asked.

'Meaning do I feel like yelling so loudly that you'd hear me on the mainland but am I fighting it down because I'm hero material through and through?' He grinned. 'Lady, if I'm in agony I'll let you know.'

'So how much pain are you in?'

'It hurts as if I have a really nasty sprain but there's no sharp jabbing. And I can feel everywhere you're touching. I checked my own toes this morning. It seems you got it back fast enough for me not to have suffered nerve damage, and there's nothing wrong now except a few torn ligaments and bruised muscles. Time alone will heal that.'

'I couldn't have put it better myself.' Christie smiled, and then thought better of it. Smiling at this man was dangerous because he smiled back, and when he did…

Whew!

'Put your clothes back on,' she said, more brusquely than was necessary. 'I'm going to the hospital now. I'd imagine you can do without your wheelchair but Grandpa has any number of walking sticks you can borrow. Keep your leg up as much as possible.'

'Yes, ma'am.' Hugo sat up, bare-legged and bare-footed and very, very male, and he was *still* laughing at her. 'You don't have a taxi on this island, I suppose?'

'In your dreams.' Then she relented and managed a smile. 'Why on earth would we need a taxi? The island's five miles wide and seven miles long. Walking's good, Dr Tallent.'

'Not with this knee.'

'So where so you want to go?'

'Down to the harbour,' he told her. 'I want to see the damage to my father's boat.'

She hesitated, and then shrugged. What was the harm, after all? There was nowhere he could run if he stole it.

'My grandfather's car is in the shed. It's old but it goes, and I'm sure he wouldn't mind lending it to you. Especially

if…' Again she hesitated, but this man was good. He was
a mind-reader.

'Especially if I took him with me?'

'Yes.' She smiled gratefully at him. He saw things, did
Hugo Tallent. He knew the hardest thing for Stan now was
the forced inactivity—the change from being a work-driven
general practitioner to an invalid all in one hit.

'It'd be my pleasure.' And then he hesitated as a soft
knock echoed through the cottage. 'Uh-oh. Visitors. I'd best
get my trousers on. I'm hardly fit for company.'

'No,' Christie agreed wholeheartedly. The sooner this
man's body was covered, the happier she'd be. 'No, Dr
Tallent, you're not.'

It was work.

Christie emerged from Hugo's bedroom to find that her
grandfather had already opened the front door. Mandy King
was standing on the doorstep. Tall and gawky, Mandy was
seventeen years old and shy as a rabbit. Her blonde hair
was dragged into two unbecoming pigtails and her shorts
and T-shirt were old and stained. She looked every inch a
tomboy, but with the promise of beauty to come.

And it would come. Christie knew her well and had sym-
pathised with the girl since babyhood. Mandy's mother was
petitely beautiful, and she agonised over her awkward
daughter. Half the reason Mandy looked like she did,
Christie suspected, was to annoy her picture-perfect mama.
There was no way she could reach the standards her mother
expected, so she refused to try.

But the girl wasn't concerned about her parents now. She
stood, dishevelled and tear-stained, on the doctors' front
step, and in her arms she cradled a scruffy, rat-faced terrier.

'What's the problem, Mandy?' Stan demanded as
Christie appeared. Stan had delivered this girl, as he'd delivered most of the islanders under forty. He shot a look at

hristie and stood back so she could see. 'What's up with
crubbit?'

It wasn't unusual that Stan knew Scrubbit-the-dog. The
hole island knew Scrubbit. When Mandy's mother had
efused to allow Mandy, then aged twelve, to keep the tiny
tray, Mandy had gone on a hunger strike that was still the
lk of the island.

Mandy's mother was strong-willed, but Mandy had been
tronger. After five days without eating or drinking, Mandy
ad collapsed, and the island doctors had finally intervened.

'She keeps the dog or you lose your daughter,' Mandy's
other had been told by Dr Stan, and that had been
andy's first major triumph over the appalling Gloria. But
ow Mandy was very much a child alone.

'Bring him in, Mandy,' Christie told her, looking down
t the dog in concern. 'What's happened?'

'He can't walk.' Mandy gulped and her hold on her pet
ghtened. 'The night before last—that was the night Ben
as nearly drowned and I was down at the harbour with
he rest of the kids. Scrubbit was with me, but he disap-
eared. Yesterday I searched and searched and I finally
ound him cowering under the wharf. But he can't walk. I
alled him out from under where he was hiding, and he
ort of dragged himself out to meet me. I think his back
egs are paralysed.'

Christie frowned. The little dog was less than six years
ld. This wasn't old age.

'Let me take him.' She stepped forward, lifting Scrubbit
arefully from Mandy's arms and setting him on the kitchen
able. This was a kitchen table-cum-operating table. With
he breakfast things removed, one good dose of disinfectant
nd the thing was transformed.

So what was wrong? The dog definitely couldn't stand.
s Christie set him down, his hindquarters sank. He obvi-
usly had strength in his forelegs—he was pushing himself

up as if he were sitting, but this was no normal sitting position. His hind legs were useless.

But he made no sound as Christie gently examined him. The small terrier gazed up at the people around him, his intelligent eyes pain-filled but trusting. Do with me what you want, his body language said. I'm in your hands.

'Mum says he'll have to be put down and she told Dad to do it.' Mandy gulped back her tears. 'I read my medical books and couldn't find anything to do for him. Nothing. I wanted to bring him to you last night, but Mum said you had too many medical emergencies and if I came near you she'd drown him straight off. And I can't pay. But I can't bear… I can't bear…'

It was too much. She sank onto a chair and buried her face in her hands. She'd been awake all night with her injured pet, she'd been up the night before with the drama at the harbour, and she was close to breaking.

'Hey.' The growly voice by the door was enough to make even Mandy look up. Dressed again in his fisher man's clothes, Hugo looked stunningly male—stunningly competent—in fact, so plain stunning he made Christie blink. 'What's happening?' he demanded.

'We have a sick dog,' Christie said briefly, shoving away these strange and unwanted sensations. Honestly, put one attractive male in her orbit and she was behaving like a schoolgirl! And she had to be a doctor. Or a vet…

She blocked Hugo firmly out, running her hands over the dog's fur and carefully examining each of his limbs. 'Don't worry about payment, Mandy,' she said softly. 'I don't charge friends.' As if he understood, Scrubbit looked up with melting eyes and Christie found her heart reaching out to him. Please…

'Don't you have a vet on the island?' Hugo asked curiously, and Christie shook her head.

'I'm the acting vet.'

That startled him. 'Do you have training?'

'I have textbooks and no choice,' she said briefly, her attention all on the dog. Hugo was still distracting—very distracting—but now was hardly the time to be distracted. 'His back legs hurt when you touch them, Mandy,' she told the worried teenager. 'Watch his face. He reacts. His front legs seem fine, though. Grandpa, can you pass me my stethoscope, please?'

Stan was before her. He'd been fumbling in a side drawer and produced it almost as she asked, acting as if it wasn't at all unusual for his granddaughter to be treating animals on the kitchen table. It was as if it was an everyday occurrence.

And Hugo could only stare, stunned by the tableau before him. This wasn't the sort of medicine he was accustomed to. There was complete silence in the room while Christie listened to her patient's heart. The whole room seemed to listen.

'His heart's OK, Mandy,' Christie told her. 'He's a strong little dog. Just hold him still while I take his temperature.' Stan handed her a thermometer and Hugo raised his brows as he saw where she put it.

'I trust that's not your normal people thermometer?' he asked dryly, and his question made Christie smile.

'Nope. I have an animal kit.'

'Thank God for that.' He frowned, thinking it through. 'You mean you do a lot of this?'

'Someone has to do it,' she told him. She motioned to Mandy. 'Mandy here has aspirations to be a vet—she's clever enough and one day she'll get there—but until that happens it's me. If not me, then who?'

Who, indeed? Hugo frowned as he waited for the results. This girl—this island doctor—had so much on her shoulders. The more he saw the less he understood how she coped. Now she withdrew the thermometer and glanced down at the results.

'Better and better,' she told Mandy, sending her a reassuring smile. 'That's almost normal. If he's been in shock it seems he's over it now.'

'I cuddled him all night,' Mandy whispered. 'Really carefully though, so I didn't move any bones. I packed him with hot-water bottles and took him to bed with me, though Mum didn't know.'

'Good for you,' Christie told her. 'Warmth was the best thing you could give him last night. It may well have saved his life.'

'But what's wrong with him?'

'I think he's been hit by a car.'

'But…' Mandy stared. 'How do you know?'

'Look at his pads.' She rolled the little dog gently over onto his back and held up a pad for inspection. The nails were almost shredded.

'It's a tell-tale sign,' she told them. 'When animals are hit they grab at the road. The night before last, with the drama in the harbour, cars were speeding all over the island. I think Scrubbit had an argument with a car and came off second best.'

'But… If he's paralysed…' Mandy gave a shattered sob, as if Christie had just told her the worst possible news. 'It'll be his spine. Mum says he'll have to be put down and she's probably right.' She raised tear-drenched eyes to Christie. 'I love him, but I don't want him to drag himself around for the rest of his life.'

Brave kid, Hugo thought. The whole scenario had him fascinated. This was about as far out of his circle as a city specialist as it was possible to be—and he wouldn't have missed it for the world.

'Let's not give up hope just yet,' Christie told her. 'If

you had him with you all last night you'll be able to tell
me a bit more. Is he able to urinate, do you know?'

'Yes.' Mandy gulped. 'This morning early… He seemed
to be getting more and more upset and I guessed what
might be wrong—he's never, ever gone inside the house.
So I carried him down to the garden and he went. I had to
hold him up.' She tilted her chin proudly. 'And he let me!
He didn't cock his leg, though.'

'That's great news,' Christie said warmly. 'The best. It
reduces the chance of internal injury no end. If he's using
the muscles down there it also lessens the likelihood of
spinal injury. Our next step is to take him up to the hospital
and give him an X-ray.'

'Does the government know you use your X-ray equipment for *dogs?*' Hugo demanded, startled, and Christie shot
him a look that said *Butt out right now.*

'No, Dr Tallent, it doesn't. Unless you plan to tell them?'

'I…' He held up his hands in mock surrender. 'No.
Heaven forbid.'

'Very wise,' she said severely, 'otherwise I'll need to
double your medical bill and charge you three times the
insurance rebate for your hospital room. Plus charge you
rent for your stay here. The islanders help fund their hospital, it's used for their needs, and if one island dog doesn't
fit into the islander needs category then I don't know what
does.' She pursed her lips. 'Scrubbit keeps the island rat
population down. As far as I'm concerned, that's eradicat-
ing a major health risk, and Scrubbit therefore gets his
X-ray. Free.'

'What reason did you use when you X-rayed Eva
Rannikin's goat?' Mandy asked cheekily, her fear receding
a little, and Christie chuckled. Great, she thought. To see
Mandy smile again was worth every spoke Hugo could
thrust in her wheel.

'Weed control,' she said smartly. 'Same thing. Brutusthe-goat is murder on thistles, and thistles cause no end of scratches to my patients.' Her smile died. 'OK, guys, we're wasting time here.' She lifted Scrubbit gently into her arms. 'Coming, Mandy?'

'Can I come, too?' Hugo asked. He wouldn't miss this for quids. 'But…aren't you booked for morning surgery?'

'The islanders know trauma takes precedence over everything else,' Christie said serenely. 'Unless there's something more life-threatening, a road-accident victim comes first. Even if it's Scrubbit.'

This whole scenario was amazing! Hugo thought. Stranger and stranger. Christie drove the short way to the hospital to keep Scrubbit from being shaken further. Once there, Hugo accompanied them to the hospital's X-ray department. He was limping, but coping fine on one of Stan's walking sticks.

To his astonishment, the nurses didn't blink at the sight of a dog being brought into the hospital. Scrubbit was X-rayed from every conceivable angle without a protest from anyone, and finally one of the nurses—Glenys—poked her nose around the door to find out what was happening.

'What's the diagnosis, Doc?'

'Broken pelvis and femur,' Christie said, holding the film to the light. 'Which is great news. I was afraid it might be his spine, but there's no sign of vertebral damage. Do I have a surgery waiting?'

'You do. There's a couple of problems, too,' Glenys told her. There was no urgency in her tone, though. Once again Hugo marvelled that people were being kept waiting for a dog, but no one seemed the least worried. Glenys was smiling at Mandy as if she were smiling at a patient—with just as much concern. 'All fixable, then?'

'I hope so,' Mandy whispered.

'I know so. Tell them ten minutes, Glenys.' Christie nodded dismissal to her charge nurse—she did have to move fast here—and then motioned for Mandy to look at the X-rays. 'See? There and there. Look at the crack across the pelvis. That break will be OK. It's not shattered or out of position and it should heal itself.' She motioned to the femur. 'This bone here, however, is completely fractured and it's what's causing the problem. It's why he doesn't want to use his hind legs. He can't use one and the other has gone out in sympathy.'

'Will he live?'

'I'm sure he will.' Christie shot a look at Hugo, a calculating look he didn't quite like. 'Especially as we have a trained anaesthetist on the island.'

'What, me?' Hugo raised his eyebrows in disbelief. He was looking at the X-ray and saw clearly what Christie was seeing—the shattered femoral head. There was no possibility that such a shattering could be repaired. In a human it'd require an artificial joint.

Did they make artificial joints for dogs?

'Do you know of any other anaesthetists lurking around here?' Christie's eyes sparkled with mischief, and she smiled across at Mandy. 'Dr Tallent's been wondering how best to pay for all the wonderful care we've been giving him. This is just the ticket.'

Then her hand reached out to tilt Mandy's chin so that the teenager's eyes met hers, and Christie's smile died. There were some questions that needed to be asked. 'Where does your mother think you are now, Mandy?' she said softly. 'What have you told her?'

'I...' Mandy looked up at Christie, and Hugo could see that the girl didn't have the capacity to lie. 'She thinks I'm at school.'

'Did she ask how Scrubbit was this morning?'

'No.' Mandy shook her head. 'She doesn't care. I guess she thinks he's dead.'

'If Scrubbit comes home better, there'll be no fuss?'

'No...except I can't pay,' Mandy told her, truthful but trustful. Her tone was almost defiant. She'd had her back to the wall before, and she was expecting a fight.

'I told you, that's no matter,' Christie assured her, with a calmness Hugo found extraordinary. He'd never met a doctor who would do this. 'But let's see if we can get over this without fuss. Your mum will have kittens if she finds you're not at school. What if I ring Miss O'Shea, and explain what's going on?'

She checked her watch. 'It's only ten now. You can appear in class and Miss O'Shea will cover for you.' Helen O'Shea, the principal of the island school, was a friend, and Christie knew she'd be on their side.

'But I don't want to leave Scrubbit...'

'Scrubbit is fine. He's not in shock. I'll give him something for the pain, I'll put in a drip to keep his fluids up and then we'll leave him to sleep. To wait won't hurt him at all—in fact, it'll be better if he's well hydrated before surgery.'

She smiled again, and her hand touched Mandy's shoulder. 'It's fine, Mandy. I promise. I need to run a people surgery now, and Dr Tallent needs to read up on small dog anaesthesia. We won't operate until this afternoon. Do you want to come back after school and watch?'

Mandy took a deep breath. 'Can I?'

'If you want to become a vet one day, it's a good beginning.'

'Oh, yes.' Mandy sounded stunned. 'As if Mum would ever let me do vet training. Fat chance. But...' She collected herself, returning to the subject of Scrubbit. 'What will you do? Operating, I mean. How will you set the bone?'

'We'll remove the femoral head,' Christie told her, adult to adult. She motioned to the X-ray. 'That's this part here. We don't have a choice. See these shards of bone?

Whatever hit him, it hit him hard. He's very lucky it's not worse. The bone's shattered and he'll never walk on it as it is, but we can remove it by taking it off here. In humans we'd put in a false joint, but in small dogs it's mostly left to a false fibrous joint will develop. The leg will be stiff but he'll be able to use it. You'll still love him if he has a limp, won't you?'

'Of course I will.' Mandy reached down and hugged her pet, her thin shoulders sagging in relief. 'I thought he'd die.'

'He won't die,' Christie promised. Her eyes creased in mischief again in a look Hugo was starting to know, and she looked over to where he was standing. 'After all, we have a specialist anaesthetist right on hand. What dog could ask for more?'

What, indeed?

Hugo left Christie to her queue of patients, then returned to the cottage and asked Stan to show him the veterinary texts. After all, refusal was out of the question—especially since Christie had inferred that speeding cars rushing down to the harbour to rescue *him* had been the cause of Scrubbit's injury.

He felt totally bemused. In fact, he was starting feel so bemused it was hard for him to open his mouth in front of the lady. This island's medical arrangements were stunning.

Stan, however, wasn't even vaguely surprised by Christie's plans. 'Sure,' he said easily. 'No worries. We've operated on everything here from a seal with a damaged flipper to a kid's pet frog.' He grinned. 'To tell you the truth, the frog died. Didn't get the anaesthetic dose right. I messed that one up, so let's see if you can do better.'

He hauled out the texts, found the relevant sections and they spent a couple of hours going through dosages and procedures and animal anatomy, with Stan enjoying himself enormously.

Stan Flemming had been one intelligent doctor, Hugo decided at the end of their time together. As a result of the stroke, his mind wandered a bit—he repeated himself or stopped talking mid-sentence, thinking he'd finished—but he was acute enough to be of enormous help. Hugo asked the right questions and Stan either knew the answers or knew where to find them. By midday Hugo was almost feeling he could face one dog anaesthetic.

Finally, as well read as possible, and feeling mutually pleased with themselves, they took Stan's old roadster from the shed and tootled down to the harbour. There they spent half an hour inspecting boat damage.

Even that wasn't enough to depress Hugo, and the unusual company gave Stan a new lease of life. As did the fact that Hugo couldn't walk any faster than he could.

'You've got no idea what it's like to have company in crippledom,' he told Hugo, pleased. 'You're wonkier than I am, boy.' And in the face of that it was hard for Hugo even to bewail his injured knee.

Finally they headed home via the tiny Briman Island shopping centre. And for some strange reason, Hugo felt great.

Knee pain, a broken boat and the prospect of operating on a dog should have put Hugo in a black mood for a week, but not now.

Why not?

Maybe it was the prospect of Christie coming home for lunch. Maybe...

She did.

Christie slipped home just after one o'clock, bright and cheerful and still feeling the effects of her abnormal amount of sleep. Or something. It must be that, she told herself, not the thought that Hugo was waiting...

She usually made lunch herself, but to her surprise

meal was already waiting for her. A pile of sandwiches had been cut from slabs of fresh bread from the island bake-house, filled with…what?

Smoked salmon and avocado, for heaven's sake!

And Stan and Hugo were beaming at her as if the pair of them had won the pools. They looked like conspirators, Christie thought, and the lightness in her heart grew and grew.

'These are not my normal cheese sandwiches,' she an-nounced, eyeing the pile with suspicion and trying hard not to think about housekeeping funds—and the fact that they'd have an extra mouth to feed for a while. This looked ex-pensive! Then, unable to help herself, she lifted a sandwich and bit. 'Yum!' The 'yum' was definitely muffled.

'It didn't come out of our housekeeping,' Stan told her, guessing her unuttered worry. 'Doris nearly had kittens when Hugo walked in and started buying up big. She had smoked salmon and caviar and avocados left from the Pierces' party last week. She thought she'd be stuck with it because they underestimated the cost and refused to take it, but Hugo bought the lot.'

'Caviar?' Christie stared.

'He bought it for dinner.' Stan chuckled, pointing a fin-ger at Hugo. 'Couldn't stop him. He reckons it's to cele-brate the dog's operation. Seems the lad has more money than sense.'

'Or the lad's incredibly grateful he can eat anything at all,' Hugo declared, helping himself to his third sandwich. 'Do have another, Dr Flemming. You deserve it.'

So Christie did, sinking down to sit at the kitchen table with her grandpa and this amazing man—this man who twinkled at her and grinned and made her feel like she'd never felt in her life before. Like…a woman?

Which was nonsense. It was because he was kind, she told herself crossly. And intelligent and intuitive and—

'I've been talking to Ben,' she said, cutting her thoughts off at the pass. They were heading in dangerous directions. 'I've let him go home.'

'I'm glad.' Hugo's twinkle died, but the warmth was still behind his eyes. He cared, Christie thought. He cared deeply abut the boy who'd saved his life, and she knew enough of the high powered life of city specialists to know that this was the exception rather than a rule. A man with warmth, who'd give the time required…

'His father told me what you'd done,' she said softly, and the warmth she'd been feeling ever since she'd walked into Ben's ward was unmistakable.

'What, half killed him?' Hugo demanded.

'Not that.' She turned to Stan to explain. 'I walked into the ward, expecting the same withdrawn, traumatised Ben of yesterday, and I found him surrounded by his mates. His whole class had come to visit.'

'I…' Hugo was looking embarrassed, concentrating on his sandwich.

'And Helen O'Shea told me whose idea it was. Hugo's. She said Hugo rang her last night—while I was sleeping, I guess—and told her that hero appreciation would be the best thing possible for Ben. It might mean making Hugo look dumber than he really was, but Hugo told her he didn't mind playing the part.'

'I don't—'

But Christie wasn't brooking interruptions. 'Ellie, our local reporter, has been in,' she told her grandfather, and she was unstoppable. She was still joyful and she was aching to talk about it. 'Hugo told Ellie he wouldn't be alive if it hadn't been for Ben, and Ben's parents must be fantastic to have produced a kid with such skills. Hugo said it as if he didn't know Ben's mum was dead. And Ellie got all choked up, and she's sending the story on to the mainland papers because she knows Ben's mum would have been so proud—'

'Have another sandwich,' Hugo said, but he was ignored.

'And Hugo himself,' Christie continued, 'told Ben he was the bravest kid he'd ever met, and he said it was almost like there must have been someone in the water, helping him, and he must have a guardian angel. And Ben's been thinking it over, and do you know what he asked? He said, 'Do you really think my mum would be proud?'' And I got all choked up too, and said, ''Absolutely. Of course.'' And then he asked, ''Do you think she's really still with me?'' It was too much for me,' Christie admitted. 'I left him to his mates and had to go wash my face for ten minutes.'

'Hey, I didn't—' Hugo was clearly embarrassed down to his borrowed socks, but Christie wasn't letting him off the hook yet.

'When I met Ben's dad in the corridor,' she went on, still talking to her grandfather but all her attention on Hugo, 'he was almost as chuffed as Ben, and he said that it's like they've been given Sue back. Just a bit. He and Ben both feel that Ben couldn't have done it alone and she's with them and she always will be. And he reckons the burden Ben's been carrying for so long has been lifted—just like that.'

Christie took a deep breath and forced her eyes to meet Hugo's across the table. Hers were shining with unshed tears. 'If you knew how hard I've worked with that boy,' she told him. 'We both have, Grandpa and I, trying to make him see that he couldn't carry his mum's death as his burden for ever. And one intuitive, sensitive discussion with you and you've done the thing. Hugo Tallent, you might be the world's worst sailor, but I could kiss you.'

He laid down his sandwich. Now this was hopeful.

'So what's stopping you?' he demanded, smiling his gorgeous, heart-stopping smile which almost had Christie wilting where she sat. 'Not me. I'd like it a lot.'

'I'll kiss Grandpa instead,' she managed, and reached over and kissed Stan on the nose. And then, for good measure and because she was feeling like she'd burst if she didn't, somehow she leaned sideways and kissed Hugo, too. Just lightly, fleetingly, a feather touch on the lips, before she sank back onto her chair and looked down at her pile of squashed sandwiches.

'Whoops...'

The emotion in the room dissolved as she choked on laughter—and then she looked back up and caught the look in Hugo's eyes and the tension zoomed in again. Because the warmth in his eyes told her that he hadn't objected to her kiss one bit, and he wouldn't mind extending the experience indefinitely.

And suddenly Christie wasn't at all sure that she didn't want it herself. What would it be like to be kissed—properly kissed—by this man?

Good grief! Get a grip, Christie Flemming...

She buried herself in her smoked salmon sandwich with a fierceness that would have been more reasonable if she hadn't eaten for a week, but Hugo's eyes stayed on her thoughtful. And she was so aware...

Lunch continued—somehow. Stan told her about the trip to the harbour and their boat inspection and their veterinary training session, and she listened but she didn't let her eye meet Hugo's again.

It was too dangerous by far.

CHAPTER FOUR

AFTER lunch, Christie saw ten more patients, most of whom, she suspected, just wanted to talk about the excitement of the near-drowning. How did she think it would affect dear Ben? What was this new doctor like? She worked her way through them all. It seemed to take forever, and there was hardly a real medical problem among them.

Finally she saw off Mr Gregg and his recalcitrant piles, filed her notes and bade her receptionist farewell. Then she was free to think about Scrubbit-the-dog.

And Hugo.

She was feeling really, really odd. Hugo had been in her thoughts all day. Every time she thought about him she felt light and bubbly, like a teenager about to go on her first date.

Which was nonsense, she told herself fiercely. In a few days he'd be gone. He'd return to practising his medicine in Brisbane, she'd work on, and that would be that. And then... *Never the twain shall meet.*

'And that's fine,' she said fiercely as she took herself through to the rear of the hospital. She used a small back room for animal surgery—using the main hospital theatre for dog operations was maybe a bit too much. 'Hugo leaving is fine by me,' she told herself. 'Of course it is. What else could it be?'

But she still felt light.

After all, *never the twain shall meet* was all very well for the future, but it didn't include the appointment in ten minutes' time when they operated on a dog together!

*   *   *

'Tell me again why we can't insert an artificial joint?'

White-coated and ready for operating, Hugo found himself feeling not a little ridiculous. Christie had gone to an inordinate amount of trouble for one small dog. The tiny theatrette was set up as well as a hospital theatre, and it looked absurd to see one sad pooch as their patient.

If they were going to all this trouble then a hip replacement had to be possible. Hugo had given the anaesthetic for any number of hip-replacement operations in his time. He rechecked the X-ray, remembered the X-rays he'd seen of human patients and thought that it would be no more complicated.

'Wouldn't an artificial joint be more useful?' he asked.

'Maybe,' Christie said briefly. She was sorting her tray ready for surgery. In a human theatre she'd have had nurses on hand, but her nurses were busy enough as it was and here she was very lucky to have Hugo. But this was just as complicated as human surgery, if not more so, because the joint was so much smaller. And also because the number of canine hip operations Christie had done—or even seen—in her medical training was approximately nil.

'So why don't we use one?' Hugo asked helpfully. The idea of a neat hip replacement in such a nice dog appealed enormously.

'Have you any idea how much a replacement human hip costs?'

'I…' He looked blank. Hmm. 'Well, no,' he had to admit. 'I don't.'

'You've never been told—because human hip replacements are subsidised by the government, and the government doesn't pay for dog hips. I'm covering the cost of medication and throwing in my labour, but I can't run to hip joints.'

'I see.' He did see. Sort of.

'Plus the fact that it'd take days to get a prosthesis here—

much less made to fit.' Christie's brows drew together in concentration and Hugo knew she was focussing almost totally on the task ahead. But still she found room to answer him.

'Think of the complications,' she said. 'All dogs are different sizes. We'd need a stainless-steel prosthesis for the femoral head, and we'd also need a high-density polypropylene socket made to fit for the acetabulum. So...' She glanced up at him. 'Where do you suppose I'd get that made on a tropical island fifty miles from the mainland?'

'It'd take a specialist kind of hobby whittler,' Hugo agreed, smiling. He held up his hands in mock surrender. 'OK, OK. In the absence of cottage industries making dog prostheses, you know best. Where do you get this knowledge, by the way?'

'Reading,' she said briefly. 'There's little else to do around here at night, and if I don't keep up with medical research then I'm finished.' She caught herself on the unexpected note of bitterness. Oh, for heaven's sake, Hugo wasn't interested in her social life—or lack of it. 'Ready?'

'I'm ready.' He was watching her strangely and the experience was unsettling. Christie welcomed the sound of Mandy's approaching footsteps with relief and it wasn't just because she'd been waiting for her.

'Here's the final member of our surgical team.' She took a deep breath, fighting to regain her composure as the teenager burst into the room. 'Hey, slow down,' she told her. 'Scrubbit's fine, Mandy. There's no rush. Would you like to give him a cuddle before Hugo puts him to sleep?'

It was an amazing piece of surgery—as amazing as Hugo had ever seen on any human. With Mandy watching, eagle-eyed but white as chalk from anxiety, Hugo intubated the little dog and then monitored his every breath as if he were the most precious patient he'd ever anaesthetised.

As, indeed, he seemed to be. Christie couldn't have cared more if it had been a child she'd been operating on, Hugo thought as he watched her work. She was carefully scrubbed and her hair was in a surgical cap. She was gowned, slippered and masked, and all he could see were those amazing green eyes.

And her fingers. She moved with precision, as if this were some long-learned procedure she'd done over and over, and her fingers were those of a skilled surgeon. Where on earth had she learned to do this, and what on earth was she doing using her skills merely on this island? he wondered. Surgery was her absolute talent.

She could be in mainstream surgery, earning a fortune, he thought as he watched her. She'd get nothing for this operation. Nothing! She and her grandfather seemed broke, and this would end up costing her money from her own pocket.

It didn't seem to be worrying her, though. Carefully, painstakingly, she cleaned the incision of every piece of shattered bone, then lined up the saw for a perfect excision arthroplasty—the complete removal of the femoral head.

In a human such a procedure would be worse than useless—the limb could never bear weight without the head and socket—but…

'He has four legs and he's not overweight,' Christie told Mandy as she worked. 'According to the experts, he'll carry this leg for a while but it'll heal with a non-painful fibrous joint. He'll learn to depend more on his strength from the other leg—in fact, he'll be fine.'

Mandy nodded. She hadn't taken her eyes from the wound once as Christie worked, and Hugo marvelled at her stoicism. Not a lot of seventeen-year-olds could have seen this messy procedure through. Even when Christie was cutting the bone—a dreadful sound—she didn't flinch.

Satisfied at last, Christie finally started closing. Hugo

checked and rechecked his monitors. If Christie was taking this seriously then so was he, and the patient wouldn't die from lack of expert anaesthetic if he could help it.

Still Mandy concentrated. She was soaking it in as if she was desperate to learn, and what Christie had said earlier in the day came floating back into his consciousness.

'Dr Flemming says you want to be a vet,' Hugo said into the concentrating silence.

Mandy glanced up at him, as though only now remembering he was real, and then went back to concentrating on what Christie's fingers were doing. 'Mmm. But there's no chance.'

'Why do you say that?' Then he grimaced as he realised the probable reason. Getting into vet school needed marks in the top one per cent of the country. How many kids dreamed of becoming doctors or vets but could no sooner achieve the university entrance requirements than fly?

But it seemed academic excellence wasn't the problem.

'It's money,' Mandy said, and went back to concentrating again. 'I guess I'll end up a fisherman's wife with six kids. Or working in the co-op, cleaning fish. Or both.' The bitterness in her voice was almost palpable and Hugo sent an enquiring glance at Christie.

Christie was relaxing—at last. It might look to Hugo as if she'd done hundreds of these types of operations, but this was an absolute first. She'd seemed calm on the outside but Hugo wasn't to know she'd been in a quiet sweat all day.

She'd spent an hour on the internet this afternoon. She'd contacted one of the mainland's leading veterinary surgeons, and he'd gone though the procedure with her over and over, sending her diagrams and instructions for every step. Her computer and the isolated medical network she belonged to over the internet was an absolute blessing.

But it had still been incredibly hard. So now she could

stand back from the table, sigh with relief—but not too deeply, as a girl had some pride—and think about Mandy

'Mandy's bright enough to get into vet school,' she told Hugo briefly, and the traces of strain were still in her voice. 'Helen O'Shea, her headmistress, tells me that with the work she's put in she's expected to come close to the top of the state.'

'It's not much use, though, is it?' Mandy whispered. Her hand was stroking her dog's wiry coat, and there was a deep sadness on her face that belied her years. Christie had taken her moment's respite and was back at work. She was now starting to immobilise the joint and dress the wound, and Mandy's thoughts were free to worry about something other than her dog. 'I keep hoping for a miracle but it's hardly worth sitting the exams,' she said sadly.

'When are your exams?' Hugo asked, and Mandy shrugged.

'In two weeks. But...'

'But?'

'It's no use. Miss O'Shea keeps saying try, try, but even with a scholarship I can't afford to live in Brisbane and go to university.' She closed her eyes. 'I've thought and thought, but I can't do it. Not yet.'

She lifted her chin then, a trace of the old defiance showing through. 'So I'll work in the co-op for two or three years and save everything, and maybe then...'

Maybe. Hugo looked at the teenager's set face for a long moment before turning back to his dials, and he glimpsed the look in Christie's eyes as she worked. She was thinking the same as he was, he decided.

Three years mind-deadening work might well clean any ambitions right out of Mandy's head. The drudgery of dead-end work and saving every cent would be too much.

'Mandy...'

'Mmm.' She wasn't looking at him. This was her probem, her body language said, and she'd deal with it without asking for sympathy.

And Hugo's gut twisted. The kid's raw courage... Christie and Mandy were of a type, he thought. They tacked overwhelming odds head-on, with all the courage in the world. Well, Mandy should have her chance.

'If you obtain the marks to get yourself into vet school,' he found himself saying, and he hadn't even thought it through properly before he said it, 'then I'll pay your expenses. Living. Travel. Textbooks and course fees. Whatever you need until you graduate as a vet, I'll pay.'

Silence. There was absolute, stunned silence in the theatrette, broken only by the soft hush of the machine providing oxygen for Scrubbit.

'It's time to reverse anaesthetic,' Christie said at last, snapping out of shock and snapping into anger. Mandy was so stunned she couldn't say a word. 'Please, Dr Tallent...'

'Of course.' Hugo slipped back into anaesthetist mode, but before he did so he gave the white-faced teenager a wink. 'Our Dr Flemming doesn't think I'm serious but, believe me, Mandy, I am. I don't make promises lightly and I've made you a promise now. Let's get you a nice fit pooch and then a great career, so you can operate on your own friends from here on in.'

'Do you have any idea what you're pledging?'

Scrubbit-the-dog's anaesthetic was safely reversed, the patient was heavily sedated, but he was breathing for himself and showing every sign of eventual recovery. Mandy was watching over him, still in stunned silence, and Christie had half dragged, half pushed Hugo out into the corridor, slamming the door behind them.

Her anger was palpable. She'd hauled off her mask. Her curls were escaping every which way from her theatre cap—Hugo badly wanted to lift the cap off and free them all—and her green eyes were flashing daggers.

'This is ridiculous. Cruel!'

'What's ridiculous?' he asked mildly, and watched the daggers flash some more. These were some fireworks! This was almost worth the promise all by itself.

'A vet course,' she said slowly through gritted teeth, enunciating one syllable at a time and speaking as if she were addressing a simpleton. 'A vet course is five years long. That's five years of living in Brisbane, which will cost a fortune. Even if Mandy gets a scholarship—and I note your incredibly generous promise didn't make a scholarship a condition of you supporting her—then there's massive costs for housing, textbooks, travel. Her parents haven't even considered it, and it's not only because they're selfish. They don't have the money.'

'And I have.'

'Oh, right.' Her anger was so great she was almost spitting. 'For six months maybe. It's a *life* we're talking about here, Hugo. A career. Mandy wants to be a vet so much that it hurts.'

'I can see that. That's why I'm making the offer.'

'If you make the offer and can't go through with it, she'll break her heart. I won't let you build her hopes like that.'

'I'm not intending to.'

And something in his voice finally got through to her. She rocked back on her heels and stared up at him for a long, long moment—and he gazed calmly back.

'You're not joking,' she said incredulously.

'No.'

'I don't believe you.'

'Believe it or not, I would never joke about anything so serious.'

Christie took a deep breath. 'Hugo...' Her eyes searched his. 'Have you really any idea what it would *cost?*'

'I put myself through med school,' he told her. 'Sure, my parents lived within shouting distance of the university so I didn't have living expenses, but we weren't rich and my brother cost my parents a fortune. I ran a part-time job and my father and I worked ourselves silly. I'd say I have a very good idea of what it costs.'

'But…'

'But what?'

'I don't understand.' She pushed the cap from her curls—finally—and raked her hair with her fingers in a gesture he was starting to recognise. 'Why?'

'Because I wish to.'

'Because you're grateful to be alive?' She shook her head. 'That'll fade, Hugo. I advise patients never to make big decisions within six or even twelve months of major trauma, and you're no exception. You'll get back to Brisbane and forget this ever happened—but then you'll have this ongoing commitment that will make you poor for a very long time.'

'It won't make me poor.'

'You might be a specialist,' she snapped, 'but if you don't have family money then you're hardly hugely wealthy. What if you want to get married? Buy a house? And you can't because you're stuck paying for some child you can hardly remember?'

'Christie, will you stop this?' His mouth curved into a teasing smile and his dark eyes mocked her. 'You'll talk me out of it if you're not careful.'

'It's better that I do it now than you discover you can't keep it up six months into Mandy's university course.' She shook her head. 'You have no idea what this course would mean to her.'

'I'd imagine it means very much what your medicine means to you,' he said softly, his smile fading. 'Or mine to me. I was so hungry for medicine you can't imagine. Or

I guess you can—I can see it in you—and Mandy has it
too. So let me do this. I take it her parents won't object?'

'To the Hugo Tallent Benevolent Foundation? No way
They'll be pleased to be shot of her.' She bit her lip. '
shouldn't say that, but her mother really is a horror.'

'I gathered.'

Her eyes were still troubled. 'Hugo, I can't let you d
this. It's too soon. You mustn't.'

'Would it make a difference to you if I told you thi
wasn't a major decision for me?' he said gently. 'I alread
run a couple of charitable bequests. I own a house and it'
not small. I have more than enough for my needs. Mandy'
education isn't going to make me poor.'

'I can't—'

'Believe it?' He shrugged. 'If it'll make you feel better
I'll put the money into a trust for her—up front. Then
can't go back on the deal and you won't have to worry.'

'Did you win the lottery?' Christie was almost speech
less.

'Yeah, right.' He grinned, relaxing. She was looking
more and more cute by the minute—and totally bamboo
zled. And…desirable? 'I'm sorry, Dr Flemming, but how
earn my money is none of your business.' If she knew
would she be like all the other women? he thought, bu
pushed the thought away as ridiculous. He was starting t
think Christie Flemming was a very different lady. 'Res
assured, however, that I have more than sufficient for m
needs, and I'm more than willing to share.'

'Hugo, if you're serious…'

'I'm serious.'

'If you knew how much I'd wanted to do this…'

'Now, there's another thing.' He frowned. 'How come
you're so broke? Doesn't this practice pay anything?'

She glared. 'You're telling me your income is your busi
ness, but now you want to ask about mine?'

He grinned at that. '*Touché*. If you don't want to tell me...'

But there was nothing to hide. 'There are five hundred people on the island,' she said simply. 'On the mainland, a list of about three thousand patients makes for a viable practice, and that's including a strong private-public mix. We have one or two wealthy retirees but that's all. There's no one else with private health insurance and the money's minimal.'

'But you're busy.' Hugo frowned.

'I couldn't cope with any more than five hundred patients with the sort of needs these people have,' she told him. 'They might not make me wealthy—or even comfortable—but they need me. The fishing community has a high risk ratio, there's more old people here than in most towns, and there's also major health problems facing our Koori community. They're only just embracing modern medicine. At the moment their life expectancy is about fifty years, and I spend heaps of time educating and counselling and—'

'And doing work that pays peanuts or doesn't pay at all,' he finished for her, and she nodded.

'That's right. It's just lucky that Grandpa and I don't mind. We can eat peanuts if we must.'

'But not peanuts tonight because it's caviar.'

'Oh, right.' She managed a smile at him, relaxing just a little. This man was totally out of her league, she was as confused as could be, but...

Maybe, just maybe she could trust him. Heaven knew how he'd acquired it, but maybe he *did* have bucketsful of money. The thought of Mandy being able to do her vet course was wonderful. So for now, if he really could do something for Mandy...

'You'd best go in and talk to her,' she told him, and for the life of her she couldn't stop her eyes misting. 'She'll be standing in there wondering whether she misheard.'

Hugo meant it. He really meant it!

And suddenly it was all too much. Before Christie coul
help herself she took his strong, warm hands into her
stood on tiptoe and kissed him soundly full on the lips.
was a solid, wondrous kiss, full of joy and bubbling wit
life and love. And she'd done it and it was finished befor
he could even respond!

'This is the most fantastic thing,' she said, stepping bac
to stare up at his stunned face. Goodness, he was lookin
almost as stunned as she felt. 'Just magic. You spread you
largesse, Dr Tallent, while I check that my hospital patient
are all behaving themselves. Give me an hour and we'll g
home and crack your caviar. And we might even top it of
with hot chocolate. I'll think of some way we can celebrate
Tonight's for living dangerously. Heaven knows wha
could happen!'

'If you say so.' His hand reached out to touch her face
and she didn't flinch as his fingers traced the line of he
cheekbone. She was so lovely. 'But, Christie…' His voic
died.

'Yes?'

'Nothing,' he said at last.

There was nothing at all that he could think of to say.

CHAPTER FIVE

CHRISTIE did her hospital round in record time, despite everyone wanting to talk about Hugo.

'He's fabulous, isn't he?' Liz demanded as Christie checked on the proud new mother. 'So what are you doing here? If I were you, I'd stick to the man like glue.'

'Can I ask why?' Christie said dryly, and Liz cuddled her baby son and threw Christie a look of mischief.

'Well, far be it from me to suggest such a thing, but wouldn't it be wonderful if Dr Tallent fell for our island doctor? Maybe he'd even move here and take some of your workload.' Then, at the look on Christie's face, she laughed and held up her hands in mock surrender. 'I know. It's a stupid thought and way too soon. But don't fail for the want of trying, kiddo!'

Which was nonsense, Christie thought savagely as she made her way back to the cottage, but her face was burning all the same. She had to haul herself back to earth. Hugo was a skilled anaesthetist. Anyone could see that he was the best! He could hold down a teaching job in a major hospital, she thought, and to believe that someone like Hugo would ever consider practising here was ludicrous.

Still…there was tonight, and she had plans. *Don't fail for the want of trying.* She wasn't trying anything—she simply intended to enjoy.

Unconsciously her hand came up to trace the line where his fingers had run down her face.

Enjoy…

She would. Because she had so little, and every moment must be savoured.

But where was he? She was working so hard on getting her face in order that it was almost a relief when Hugo wasn't in the cottage.

'I don't know, but he's not here,' Stan told her. On Mondays he and an elderly companion played chess over steak and red wine down at the pub, and he was getting himself ready to go.

'What have you done with him?' Christie asked, bemused.

'You sound like you suspect me of locking him up.' Stan chortled. 'Maybe that's not such a bad idea. Put him in chains and throw away the key. If we could get a decent young fella like Hugo to practise with you on the island...'

'In our dreams.' Christie gave a half-hearted smile. The whole island was hallucinating here.. 'This practice hardly pays for one doctor, never mind two. And he's used to a great lifestyle. The man makes serious money.' Briefly she outlined what Hugo intended doing for Mandy, and Stan stared.

'Well, I'll be a monkey's uncle,' he said at last. 'I knew specialist salaries were big, but not that big.'

'He must do something apart from hospital anaesthetising,' Christie agreed. 'Maybe he runs one of those pain clinics where the wealthy come for regular brief consultations and he makes a mint, doing nothing.'

There were clinics—and doctors—who pulled in the money by doing just that, and both Stan and Christie knew it. They looked at each other and Christie could see that her grandfather didn't want that to be the source of Hugo's wealth any more than she did.

But why should she care?

It was none of her business how Hugo made his money, she thought savagely. He'd said so, and he was right.

But... Where was he?

Doug Connor arrived to collect Stan. Bemused, she made

her way back to the hospital. She checked each ward, half expecting Hugo to be gossiping to one of the patients, and then she checked on Scrubbit again. The little dog was sleeping peacefully, but he was alone. With Hugo's grand plan before her and university beckoning, Mandy would have headed straight for her textbooks.

Maybe Hugo had gone with Mandy to talk to her parents—but how? With his gammy knee he could hardly walk, and Grandpa's car wasn't missing. Mandy could well have walked the mile and a half home, but Hugo couldn't.

'Where is he, Scrubbit?' she asked, but the dog hardly stirred. She had him heavily sedated. He'd pull out an intravenous line without sedation and he must have fluids and an antibiotic overnight. Tomorrow, however, she suspected there'd be no stopping him. Scrubbit was one wiry pooch.

'I'll bet you'll go to Brisbane with her,' she whispered. 'Even if she stows you away in her luggage...'

Where was Hugo?

She turned, and as she did so she caught sight of a pile of paper on her desk. It had been days since she'd used the desk, but it was covered now with a wad of paper she didn't recognise.

Curious, she lifted the top page. The paper was covered with handwritten notes—a detailed outline of that afternoon's operation.

What on earth...?

She read on, fascinated. Detailed was an understatement. The notes omitted nothing. Hugo had put down full medication, step-by-step procedures, the minor hitches that had occurred, the sound of the saw, the look on Mandy's face...

This was bizarre!

The door opened behind her.

'Whoops,' Hugo said into the silence—and she jumped a foot. 'Caught.'

'H-hi,' she managed weakly, shoving the notes back on

the desk. Then she pulled herself together. Oh, for heaven's sake, this was *her* desk. It was *her* writing paper, *her* operation, *her* patient.

So what was he doing, writing about it?

'Are you some sort of spy?' she demanded, gesturing to the notes, and he grinned.

'Oh, no!' He gave a dramatic groan and there was a deepening of the lurking laughter behind those gorgeous eyes. 'You've guessed. I'm on a mission from Interpol to discover why the dogs on this island are taking over the world. And now I've discovered your dire secret. You replace bone with Kryptonite. And, lo! Superdogs!'

This man was seriously crazy. Christie took a step back and shook her head in disbelief as she found herself laughing with him. She'd never met a man like this. He kept her in a ripple of laughter—just to look at him made her feel warm all over.

So play along with him. Somehow… 'Oh, right. Any minute now Scrubbit's going to leap into his telephone box and emerge in his Superman… I mean Superdog costume,' she agreed. Laughter and warmth aside, she was still puzzled. 'Hugo, why—?'

'I just like remembering,' he said, folding the notes and tucking them firmly into his shirt pocket. 'In case…'

'In case any stray dogs with fractured pelvises wander into your Brisbane clinic and you need to deal with them?'

'That's the ticket,' he said cheerfully, and suddenly the subject was closed. There was something about the set look to his mouth—the fading laughter—that told her any further enquiries weren't welcome.

She gave an inward shrug. If he wanted to take notes she had nothing to hide, she thought. Except the odd discrepancy in who exactly took her medications. She glowered.

'You're sure you're not a government official here to check me out?'

His brows lifted in mock interrogation. 'Would that worry you? What on earth would I have to report you about?'

'I don't know.' She shrugged. 'I guess…heaps of things. It's a constant nightmare that some officious person will come here and check the running of this practice. If you were to report on dog X-rays, for instance, or discover that I gave Bert Soren two lots of antibiotics last week…'

He gave her a sideways, thoughtful look, but the twinkle returned.

'OK, Dr Flemming. Out with it. Overdosing on antibiotics, aided and abetted by your family doctor, is a dire crime. Tell all. Why did you supply Bert's habit?'

'His cow's habit.' She tried to keep a straight face but failed miserably. Hugo's laughter was too infectious to resist. 'Bert had an infected ingrown toenail, but before he could take his prescribed antibiotics his cow gashed herself on some barbed wire. Therefore Bert gave *his* pills to the cow and expected me to give him more. So, with the consequence of a spreading infection from a really nasty toenail, I did just that.' She peeped a glance at him, throwing herself on the mercy of the court. 'There you have it. I've confessed all.'

He grinned. 'Nice confession, Dr Flemming.' He reached out and tilted her chin so she was forced to look at him directly, and his touch sent a tingle right down to her toes. But he was still laughing. 'It's a pity I can't use it. If I'm a government official, where are my suit and tie and clipboard?'

'There is that,' she said thoughtfully, trying to tell her toes they weren't tingling at all! 'A proper government official would never have left his yacht without his clipboard. Drowning or not drowning.'

'So it looks like Bert's cow will get away with her ill-gotten gains. Didn't the antibiotic give her a bellyache?'

'You know, I didn't ask. I told Bert to take yoghurt with his pills—I always advise yoghurt to counter penicillin side effects—but I guess the cow can make her own. Yoghurt, I mean.'

But what *did* she mean?

Oh, for heaven's sake, what was she talking about? Yoghurt? She wasn't thinking about yoghurt, she realised dazedly. Hugo was forcing her eyes to meet his and there was a link between them that was growing by the minute. Crazy...

'I guess she can at that.' Then his lazy smile gentled, he took her hands in his and he continued to meet her look head on. And her toes tingled all over again.

'Dr Flemming, can you cease getting your knickers in a twist here?' he said softly. 'I'm not threatening you—or Scrubbit—or even Bert Soren's cow—in any way at all. I'm simply taking notes. Now, does that caviar await?'

She still didn't understand why he'd taken the notes, but the warmth of his hands holding hers, the feel of him, the way he smiled at her... Well, it would have taken a stronger woman than Christie to keep probing.

In truth, she couldn't think of anything to ask at all. His notes had become an unimportant blur. All she could think of was his touch. It wasn't just her toes that were tingling now. She was tingling all over, right to the tips of her ears.

Food! Tea! Prawns... That was why she'd been looking for him, she told herself desperately. Get back to the matter in hand...

'I—I sort of had a better idea,' she said diffidently, managing to pull her hands away. He released her, but there was a sense of reluctance—as if he felt the pull as strongly as she did.

'What?'

'We can hardly make a meal of just caviar,' she told him, somehow hauling herself back together enough to make her voice work. 'I wondered...I wondered if you might like to go prawning?'

'Prawning?' It was so unexpected it caught him off balance.

'The prawns are running,' she told him. Maybe it was a silly idea, but she hadn't been prawning for years, and if he'd never done it... He'd only be here for another couple of days, she told herself. She could enjoy his maleness—his laughter and his presence—while she could. Savour every last minute of his visit. 'It's such a dark and moonless night, it's perfect for prawning.'

'A dark and moonless night...' He grinned, and went straight into dramatic mode. 'Upstairs, the maid screamed,' he intoned dirgefully. 'The butler roamed, the hounds bayed and blood dripped from the ceiling. Meanwhile, back at the hospital... Are you sure you want to go prawning with me, Dr Flemming?'

Was he never serious? But, yes, she was sure. She was surer and surer by the minute.

'Meanwhile, back at the estuary, the prawns are running,' she said severely. 'And I really like prawns. To eat, I mean. They go perfectly with caviar.'

'I expect they do,' he said faintly. 'But isn't the weather a bit rough?' The wind was howling around the little hospital, and the seas were still pounding.

'The estuary is sheltered,' she told him 'That's why the kids were there and saw you trying to drown yourself. The cliffs form a shelter where the creek runs into the harbour entrance. If we go there tonight we could get ourselves a really good catch.'

'Why?' His brows furrowed together. 'Why tonight?'

Why, indeed? Christie floundered a little, but she might as well explain. After all, he'd be gone in a couple of days and she didn't have to see him again. She could afford to lose a little dignity with this man.

'I used to go prawning as a kid,' she told him. 'But since I came back as a doctor, I don't get asked. Grandpa and I have the gear—we used to sneak off and prawn ourselves—but…'

'You can't since Stan's stroke.'

'No. And whenever I suggest to one of the islanders that I'd like to going prawning I end up with a bucket of prawns left on my doorstep. They're happy to *give* me prawns, but they don't see prawning as my role.'

'That's crazy.'

'Maybe not,' she told him. 'I'm supposed to be here at the hospital, you see. That's where they like me. If someone goes prawning and cuts themselves, then they're happier if I'm here waiting to sew them up, rather than risking my neck prawning with them. And…'

'And?' He was trying to see.

'And if I do insist on going,' she said hesitantly, 'because I'm the doctor I'm given the best net and the best spot near the light. If I don't catch more than anyone else then they worry and give me some of theirs, and it's just…'

'Not the same as when you were a kid?'

'Nothing ever is,' she said, grateful that at least he was trying to see. 'But with you…'

'I won't patronise you. I'm another doctor so I won't hold you in the least respect, and you could beat me hands down at prawning because I have a gammy leg.'

She chuckled. 'Of course. I hadn't thought of the winning angle. But with your leg… I was thinking. It's no problem. Grandpa and I have a boat. We can row out into the estuary—it's shallow enough to push if we must. Then we'll anchor and drop the light overboard. You can sit in the boat and net prawns for all you're worth. Who knows? You might even beat me.'

He thought it through. It sounded intriguing, and if there was one thing Hugo Tallent was into it was intriguing experiences. Especially with a woman like this! 'But can we do that?' he asked. 'I mean, aren't you on call?'

'I'm always on call,' she said wearily. 'But for tonight...' She motioned to the satellite phone she had buckled at her waist. 'Let's take a chance and see if it stays quiet.'

'Let's do that,' Hugo said softly, and there was a strange look on his face, replacing the laughter she was growing accustomed to. 'Let's take a chance. OK, Dr Flemming. Lead the way.'

They had three magic hours, and Hugo had never before experienced anything like those hours.

Once beneath the shadows of the cliffs, the wind dropped like magic. It became a balmy summer night, with the sky black and almost moonless. A faint sliver of a crescent moon hung low to the east, but it wasn't enough to attract the prawns away from their light.

Christie was in charge. Hugo was content to row the boat where directed, and then sit and watch while Christie organised.

To attract the prawns, she used an underwater lantern. The old boat, pushed out of the boatshed and rowed out into the centre of the estuary, was a platform from where they could sink the floodlight. The light faced upwards so that the prawns were attracted to it and they could be seen as they swam across the beam.

Hugo was spellbound. His damaged knee meant he had to stay in the boat—he didn't want to risk wrenching it again—but he held his net and scooped up prawn after prawn.

And he watched Christie. Mostly he watched Christie.

It was as if she'd shed an outer skin as she'd launched the boat, he thought as he watched her. She was wearing ancient shorts, battered leather sandals and a tattered windcheater. She'd slipped over the side of the boat as soon as they'd anchored and was now standing waist deep in water, scooping up her prawns with a determination built of hunger. Or so she told him.

'Come on, keep netting,' she told him. 'You eat what you catch, so you'll be very, very hungry if you don't rattle your dags...'

'"Rattle your dags"?' he said faintly. 'Do I know what that means?'

She chuckled. 'It means hurry—but if you want a literal explanation, head to a shearing shed. Back to work, Dr Tallent.'

So he netted—but still he was focussed on her. He knew what the expression 'rattle your dags' meant. He'd just never heard a woman use it. The women who surrounded him would die rather.

He gave a rueful grin, remembering some of the women he'd been escorting lately. Every artifice in the book had been thrown at him since fame and fortune had hit. Who would have thought that a chit of a girl, standing waist deep in water and throwing shearer's cant at him, could do what no other woman came close to?

'Aren't you cold?' he asked from the comfort of the boat. Not a single woman he knew would do this, he decided—stomp around in waist-deep water looking like Orphan Annie, all for the sake of a few prawns.

'No. Aren't you hot?' she retorted. She reached down for a scoop of water and her eyes glimmered at him. 'Want to cool off?'

'No, thank you, ma'am.' Or maybe he did. The water looked incredibly inviting, and so did the girl. But—

But suddenly there was trouble.

Christie gave an ear-splitting yell, and suddenly the water around the boat turned to foam as she kicked out in horror. White water sprayed everywhere! *'Yow!'* Her scream could probably be heard in the middle of next week!

'Christie, what…?'

'Get it off me!' She was falling backwards into the water and thrashing wildly upwards. 'No! *No!*'

Hugo stood up in the boat and it lurched precariously as he tried to see. He couldn't. All he could see was foam and thrashing limbs—but a man had to do what a man had to do.

In one swift movement Hugo leapt overboard, stood up and steadied himself. He seized the thrashing girl and lifted her high in his arms, and then, by the light of the underwater lantern, he could see clearly what the problem was, though it was waving so wildly it was only an impression.

An octopus was hanging from her ankle.

'Ow! Ow, ow, ow!'

Christie was waving her leg like a wild woman, and yelling as if the hounds of hell were after her, but the creature clung on. She scarcely noticed she'd been lifted. Writhing in Hugo's arms, her leg was out before her and tentacles were flying everywhere.

'No!' She was yelling and laughing and spluttering with sea water all at the same time. 'Hugo, help! *No!* You revolting thing, get off!' And with a final, fierce yell—and kick—the octopus went flying upwards, landing in the water about four feet from them.

It had been more terrified than Christie. By the light of the lantern they saw it bunch its tentacles in slimy horror and scuttle seaward as if its life depended in it. And that was the last they saw of it.

'Oh, thank heaven!' Christie was still writhing in Hugo's arms as if she couldn't believe it had gone. 'Of all the disgusting things…'

'Do they sting?' Hugo still held her close, trying frantically to think back to his medical-school days. What were the venomous sea creatures? Portugese men-of-war…stone fish…blue ringed octopus…

'Keep still, Christie,' he ordered in his best doctor's voice. 'Let me see.'

And then, as she finally stilled…

'You're hurt!' He could see a trickle of blood on her bare ankle. Hell! 'Christie…'

'I kicked myself,' she said indignantly, laughing up into his worried face. 'I tried to kick it but I kicked myself instead. Just lucky for the stupid octopus.' She took a deep, indignant breath. 'I bet it's not even bruised. Oh, for heaven's sake, if I wasn't such a baby I could have caught it and we could have had calamari for dinner as well. It was a little one so it would have been really tender. Prawns and caviar and squid…'

It floored him.

He stood with Christie in his arms and he felt stranger than he'd ever felt in his life before. She was dripping wet, she was laughing up at him, her curls were soaking and her bedraggled clothing was clinging like another skin.

She was absolutely bewitching, he thought.

And suddenly—suddenly, he wanted to kiss her more than he wanted anything else on earth.

Most women—the women he knew in his other life— would have wound their arms around him and clung and held up their lips to be kissed.

But that was money talking—and fame. Christie didn't have a clue who he was, he told himself. There was no reason for her to want to be kissed, and apparently she didn't. She was still laughing and, instead of holding him tight, of responding to his need and using body language to ask to be kissed, she was turning within his hold to search the water.

'I've lost my net.' It was as if she were lying on a platform—not in his arms. 'Darn, I had at least six really big prawns in there. Oh, Hugo, there it is. Let me go…' And before he could stop her she'd launched herself out of his arms and was swimming strongly away from him across the estuary to catch up with her net, which was floating seawards with the tide. She was abandoning his arms as if his hold meant nothing.

The sensations were amazing. He could only watch her, open-mouthed, while she caught it, found her feet and held her net up in triumph.

'There's three prawns left in it,' she called in triumph. 'And they're really fat ones.'

'Great,' he said faintly. He dragged his eyes—some-how—from this amazing woman and checked the bucket in the boat. 'There's more than enough for a feed here. You want to call it quits?'

He must have sounded strange.

'Did you hurt your leg?' she asked with swift concern. She swam back to him in the shallow water, holding her net before her. As she reached him she rolled over, put her nose under the water and checked his knee by the light of the underwater lantern. Then her nose surfaced and she grinned. 'I'm sorry, Dr Tallent,' she said in the tone of a doctor making a grave prognosis, 'but I'm afraid your dressing's all wet.'

'I imagine it must be,' he said dryly, his sense of unreality deepening with every minute, 'since it's under water.'

'No matter.' She was like a rubber ball, he thought, bouncing every which way. 'I had the forethought to bring us both a change of clothes. Wasn't that clever?'

'Very clever.' Hugo didn't have a clue what she was talking about. Worse, he didn't have a clue what was happening to him. He felt like he'd been dragged into a movie set and left to wallow—while the cameras rolled on around him.

'I figured we could eat on the beach,' she told him. 'The caviar's all packed.'

'Really?'

'Really.' Christie emptied her net into the bucket and eyed her wobbly old boat with concern, worrying about how Hugo would get back in. 'Can you hoist yourself into the boat with your sore knee, or do you want me to get in and pull you up?'

She would, too, he thought. There was nothing this woman wouldn't attempt—if she had to. 'I'm fine,' he said, appalled by the thought of being lifted by a woman.

'You're not, you know,' she said seriously. 'Of all the stupid things… Rescuing me from a man-eating octopus wasn't the most sensible knee-repairing act to do. I shouldn't have brought you here.'

'I wouldn't have missed it for the world,' he said, and he meant every word.

And then some, he thought as he looked down at her. And then some…

Dinner was served on the beach, sheltered still from the wind by the lee of the cliff. The water here was lapping gently onto the estuary shoreline. There was a distant murmur of waves from the harbour mouth, where the cliff face ended and the storm could vent its fury on the sea, but in the shelter of the cliffs the winds might as well not have existed.

Christie obviously knew the place well. They rowed to the shoreline and then tugged their boat up onto the sand. Christie hauled a pile of gear from plastic bags and set to work with brisk efficiency.

'Dry clothes,' she told him, tossing him a pile. 'Courtesy of Mary-anne, though I gather Dave's wife has retrieved yours from the yacht and is in the process of washing them. We'll leave the lantern off while we change. You look that-away and I'll look this. Thus, modesty will be preserved.'

It was. Bemused, Hugo did as he was told—what else was a man to do?

His bemusement deepened by the minute, if bemusement was the right word. In fact, he didn't know how on earth to describe himself. He was so far off balance he was glad of Stan's walking stick, and it had nothing to do with his injured leg.

And when she flicked on the lantern Hugo saw that Christie was back in her wonderful crimson sweater and was wearing a clean pair of jeans. She turned her attention to the fire—and he caught his breath at the sight of her. In that sweater...

It was the way he'd first seen her.

But she wasn't noticing the effect she was having on him. She couldn't tell the way his gut kicked at the sight of her neatly denimed backside leaning over her fire.

She was so sure of herself, he thought. So self-contained. A dozen sticks, a pile of newspaper and a match, and she had the fire blazing. Then she set up a stand over the flames and scooped a billy of sea water, while all the time he watched, like a schoolboy with his first crush.

'The sea water's for the prawns,' she told him as she hung the billy on its stand. She appeared not to notice the fact that he hadn't moved. Maybe she was putting it down to his bad leg, though he was past feeling pain! 'Meanwhile, toast and caviar,' she continued. 'Yum.'

It was, too. They toasted bread on an ancient blackened toasting fork—two forks, in fact, so they could lie side by side on the sand and hold their toast to the flames. Spread liberally with his caviar, Hugo had never tasted anything so delicious. It was a night of firsts.

But... 'You wait till you taste my prawns,' Christie told him. As they'd been lying side by side by the fire, he'd been increasingly, incredibly aware of the warmth and nearness of her body, and when she jumped to her feet to fetch the prawns he was aware of a stab of loss so sharp it was as much as he could do not to protest.

Somehow he didn't make the sound. She was so unaware, he thought, so oblivious to the sexual chemistry he believed was building all the time, that it surely must only be on his side!

So he forced himself to lie still while she emptied her prawns into the boiling water, waited a whole two minutes—'any more and they'll be tough as old boots'—then drained them and settled again beside him.

What followed was a very messy half-hour—peeling each prawn, tipping the shells into the fire, dressing each with a touch of lemon juice and eating them from their fingers.

He'd never known food could taste this good, but how much was the food, how much was the setting and how much was the girl beside him he couldn't tell. The prawns were fabulous, the night was warm, the sand was still sun-warmed from the day—and the firelight played over Christie's face as she concentrated on peeling her prawns and popping each one into her mouth...

Gorgeous, gorgeous, gorgeous.

It wasn't the night Hugo was thinking of. It was the girl.

Finally she noticed his preoccupation.

'What?' She ate her twentieth prawn—give or take five or six—rolled over onto her back and sat up, twinkling down at him but demanding an answer.

'What do you mean—what?' he asked, startled.

'You've been staring at me.'

'I have not!'

'You have, too. And I don't know why you should—unless it's to gain some tips. I'll have you know I'm a very elegant eater of prawns, while you, Hugo Tallent...'

'What's wrong with the way I eat prawns?'

'You slurp.'

'I do not!'

'You do.' She lifted a prawn, peeled it—her eyes on him

all the time—then popped the soft flesh into her mouth. And bit. Then she held up one prawn tail. 'See this?'

'Yes, but—'

'It's empty. I shell the whole thing,' she said serenely. 'But you—you just shell most of the body and then you get the tail and suck. And it makes a noise. See...' And she proceeded to demonstrate.

'Christie—'

'It's the difference between surgeons and anaesthetists,' she told him kindly. 'You'd suck at skin grafts.'

'Gee, thanks.' He hesitated. 'Did you do surgery?'

'First part,' she told him. 'I was thinking of it as a career—and then Grandma died.'

'So you came here.'

'Why would I not?' She lay back on the sand, linked her hands behind her head and gazed up at the stars. 'It's the best place in the world and the people here need me. What more could a girl ask?'

'What, indeed?'

And what more could he ask than this?

It was too much. The look on her face. The warmth. Her very presence. There was no way he could resist this girl. Unbidden, he turned and looked down at her. His hands rested on her shoulders and she looked gravely up at him, her face a question in the firelight.

'Christie...'

'Mmm.' Her eyes were thoughtful, he decided, like she was watchful for what would happen. Not frightened. Just...watchful.

'I'd like to kiss you,' he said gently, and her eyes glowed in the dark. There was a look in them now he didn't understand at all.

'I bet I'd taste of prawns,' she said simply. That was all. No protest. Nothing.

'I bet I do, too.'

She twinkled up at him. 'Want to find out?'

Want to? Did he ever! And suddenly he didn't need to want any further. She was reaching forward, holding him to her and he was rolling back with her onto the warm sand.

He didn't need to find out a thing. Their lips were meeting in a kiss that felt like it could last for ever.

A life shouldn't have the capacity to be changed in one moment. It shouldn't. But once Hugo held her in his arms...once his mouth claimed hers... One kiss in the firelight and he knew that it had. Irrevocably.

She was like no other woman he'd ever kissed, he thought, dazed. For a start she tasted of prawns and campfire smoke and sea water, and maybe that was a difference in itself. But the feel of her mouth... It was like a natural linking of his body—an extension of who he was.

Or maybe he'd had a vacuum within himself which had been there for ever but he hadn't known. And suddenly that vacuum was filled and it felt right.

It felt wonderful.

His arms were tight around her, holding her oversized sweater but feeling the delicious curves of her body against him. She was every inch a woman, every inch desirable, and he wanted her so much!

His body was hers, he thought blindly if only she'd take it. She was a witch, with a capacity to put him under a spell that was as real as it was unbreakable. This night. This place...

This woman.

And she was responding. He searched her mouth and felt her lips gently part, welcoming him into her. Her own hands were holding, clinging, pulling her body tighter to him as if her need was as great as his.

Which it must be. It *must*.

Christie...

She was drowning in pleasure.

All through this evening she'd known that if he wanted to make love to her she'd welcome him. She'd never met a man who'd made her feel like Hugo did—and in three days he'd be gone.

She was twenty-eight. She was Briman Island's spinster doctor, now and for ever, and men like Hugo…

There were no men like Hugo for Christie. He was one of a kind—her kind—but she knew that there was no future for them together. Her life was here, with her people, and it was a life alone.

For tonight, though… For whatever glorious reason, Hugo was lying with her on this beach, his arms were holding her close and his mouth was on hers.

She'd take her fill of this man. She must. Because in three days he'd walk away and the memories must last her for ever.

'Hugo…'

'Mmm.'

Her hands reached under his sweater and with shock he felt her fingers touch the naked skin of his chest. Her fingers were almost pleading.

'Hugo.'

Nothing. She wanted nothing that he couldn't give. The word had been a sigh of pleasure—nothing more—of aching, searing pleasure—and as his hands searched for her breasts, found their gentle swell and gloried in the feel of her, he knew that for the two of them this night was right.

There was only now…

Only, of course, tonight included medicine.

When had it not? The islanders had kept their needs at bay for as long as they could, but three hours was long enough.

For a long moment Hugo didn't hear the phone, but he felt Christie stiffen in his hold, he was aware that the link was somehow broken and he gave a groan of protest.

But then he, too, heard it, and as he did Christie pulled away, dishevelled and lovely. Inches apart, she closed her eyes for one long moment. It was as if she was collecting herself—remembering where and what she was.

Turning again into Dr Flemming, island doctor.

'It'll be a wrong number,' Hugo whispered, pushing her hair out of her eyes with his long, strong fingers and smiling at her with such an expression that all she wanted to do was melt into him again. But then he sighed and rose, pulling her after him. Hugo, too, understood the medical imperative.

'Go on, my love. Answer your call. Tell them to take two aspirin and have a nice cup of tea—and then you come back to me.'

She smiled at him, her smile a trace uncertain. What had he said? *My love?*

No matter. It couldn't matter now. She was back to being a doctor.

She hauled her addled thoughts together and went down to the boat to find the phone.

CHAPTER SIX

Two aspirins and a cup of tea couldn't help Don Parker.

'He's dead.' Emily, Don's daughter, was almost hyster-ical on the other end of the line. 'Christie, my dad's dead.'

'Oh, Em…'

'Dear God, it's my fault.' Emily was sobbing so hard that Christie could hardly make out what she was saying. 'I always come. Every night I come. But tonight I didn't because he told me my cooking was dreadful and I should be ashamed. He's been in such a bad mood! And I was so upset… So I didn't come and now… I phoned to say good-night and he didn't answer. I thought he must be punishing me but I couldn't relax so I came over, and he's dead. He must have been upset when I didn't come and—'

'Hey, Emily, don't do this to yourself.' Christie's voice was soft and calming, but Hugo, listening, said a mental farewell to his lovely evening. Her voice said, yes, this was serious. 'Wait until I come before you figure what's hap-pened,' she was saying. 'Are you sure he's dead?' She'd had instances before when she'd been called to a corpse and had ended up tucking them into bed for the night.

'I…' Emily swallowed and caught herself. 'I'm sure. He's…he's just…his eyes… He's dead. I know he is.'

'OK. Is anyone with you?'

'No.'

'Ring Mrs Whitten. Your dad has her number on the pad above his phone. She's just next door, Emily, and I know she's home. Have her come over and stay with you. And ring your husband. I'll be there in twenty minutes.'

'Twenty minutes…' There was a long gulping breath at

the end of the line and then a tearful sob. 'Oh, Dr
Flemming, I so hoped…but they said at the hospital that
you wouldn't be available until morning.'

'I'm always available,' Christie said, and there was a
note of resignation in her voice that she could only hope
the woman didn't hear.

But she couldn't suppress it.

'We'll both go.'

'You don't need to.' They were rowing back across the
estuary. Christie's experience in a rowing boat matched
Hugo's strength, so they took an oar apiece, rowing silently
back to the boatshed and to duty beyond. 'Don's place is
just past the hospital. I'll drop you at our cottage on the
way.'

'I'm coming,' he said softly, watching her as she rowed.
Her face was set and grim. It was as if she'd been expecting
this all evening. Expecting an end to pleasure.

She worked so hard, he thought as he watched her. She'd
so wanted to go prawning, and now this! Hell, more and
more he was wanting to do something for this woman.
Lighten her load a little.

While she'd been catching prawns she'd dropped years
from her age, he'd thought. She was still a girl underneath
this load of responsibility she'd shouldered—a lovely,
laughing girl who'd felt like…

Whoa…

Slow down, he told himself. That way is deep water.

But the thought refused to go away. The ache was becoming a need.

She shouldn't let him come. She should insist that he stay
at the cottage—after all, what use could he be in examining
a corpse? Don had suffered from a heart condition for
years. This wasn't unexpected. It would involve a simple

examination, organisation of the island undertaker and then time with Emily.

There'd be nothing for Hugo to do.

But…

She couldn't protest, she decided as she rowed. This man seemed willing to spend time with her, and the way she was feeling she would take any part of him that he was prepared to give. For three more days…

Don was definitely dead—there was no doubt about it. Emily, a small, mousy woman in her late forties, led them into the sitting room and choked back sobs as Christie knelt beside Don's chair and gently saw what had to be seen.

He'd died peacefully. That was one blessing at least. He'd been sitting beside his fire, the television was still on and he'd obviously been watching. His head had simply slumped forward and he hadn't moved.

His hands were resting peacefully on his knee. There had been no attempt to rise or try to reach the phone, or even jerk in pain.

'It must have been very fast, Emily,' she said softly, looking up at the distressed woman. Hugo was standing silently in the doorway, leaving it to her but taking it all in. The next-door neighbour was hovering beside Emily, trying to comfort her, but comfort was a long way away.

'But it's the first night since Mum died that I haven't been,' Emily sobbed. 'The first night for years. I always bring him his dinner. It was just…last night he was so nasty and Mark—my husband—said I shouldn't let him keep talking to me like that. So just for once I stood up to him and said, "make your own dinner then, Dad." And he waited and waited and got upset that I didn't come and then had a heart attack…'

'If he was in any pain he would have at least tried to reach the phone,' Christie told her.

'No, he wouldn't.' Emily shook her head, her distress increasing by the minute. 'He would have just sat in that chair, rigid with anger, getting angrier and angrier all the time that his dinner wasn't here, and it would have killed him. *I* killed him!'

'I doubt that very much.' Hugo moved forward at that, to stoop by the body, edging Christie aside. 'Emily, I'm Dr Tallent. Would you mind if I examine your father? Do you mind, Dr Flemming?' At the shake of her head his hand came up and gently touched the dead man's face, closing his eyes and then carefully feeling the skin around his lower jaw and neck. 'Emily, what time do you normally bring your father's dinner?' he asked.

'I…' She was almost beyond speech. 'I guess about seven.'

'That's three hours ago.' Hugo nodded. 'Christie, do you have a thermometer?'

'Yes.' She opened her doctor's bag which she'd brought in, not because she'd expected Don to need it but because she'd thought Emily might well need something to calm her. 'Here you are. But why…?'

'Let's just see.' He gently manoeuvred the dead man so that he could slip the thermometer between his arm and chest. 'Christie, there's a room thermometer on the wall. Check it, will you? I want to know the air temperature.'

'Sure.' She was puzzled. What was he doing? But all she could do was check the room temperature as he'd asked, and then watch. When Hugo Tallent worked he was a man in charge of his world, and his air of authority was absolute. She had the sense to let him be.

And in three minutes she knew. He lifted the thermometer away from Don's body, checked the reading and turned to Christie.

'What's the room temperature?'

'Seventy-five.'

'There you go, then.' He rose and crossed to Emily. Lifting her hands from her eyes, he forced her to meet his. 'Emily, look at the thermometer,' he commanded. 'Can you read it?'

'I...' She gave a watery sniff. 'Yes. I guess.' She focussed. 'Eighty-eight.'

'That's right,' he said softly. 'Your father's body temperature is eighty-eight. It's not room temperature so we know your dad hasn't been dead for too long. But he's starting to feel cool to the touch, and his temperature has dropped from the ninety-six or ninety-seven it's supposed to be.'

'I don't understand.' Misery aside for the moment, she was just plain confused.

'When death occurs, the human body drops in temperature no more than between one and two degrees an hour,' he said. 'The only exception is when you have extreme conditions, but this is a warm room, so two degrees would have to be the maximum rate of cooling here. If your dad's temperature has dropped from ninety-six to eighty-eight, he's been dead for at least four hours and probably longer. That's backed up by the fact that his muscles have started to stiffen—it was hard for me to close his eyes. It's my guess, Emily, that your dad died at about four or five this afternoon—long before he even knew for sure that you weren't coming.'

'But—'

Hugo his head. 'No buts. The fire's died right down—he must have stoked it just before he died and maybe that amount of exhaustion was all it took for his heart to fail. But he didn't feel a thing, and it was his time to die.' He smiled gently at her, took her hands and motioned to the half-drunk glass of beer beside the chair. 'He certainly wasn't hungry or thirsty. Did your father enjoy watching the cricket?'

'I…yes.' Emily was all at sea, and Christie could only watch and wonder as the distress was replaced by something else. Acceptance?

'This afternoon nearly every hospital television was tuned to the cricket,' Hugo told her. 'It was a fantastic one-day match, and Australia was winning. I caught some of it myself. If your dad had been watching he'd have been on the edge of his seat. He'd have been watching great cricket, he'd have been excited, he'd have got up to stoke the fire— if he'd been suffering from heart failure then he'd have felt chilly, but the fire would have stopped that—and then he'd have settled down again. He had his beloved cricket and a beer in his hand and a fire before him. What more could a man ask? And what better way for an old man to go?'

Emily blinked, swallowed and blinked some more. 'You're…you're sure?' she whispered.

'I'm sure.' And by Hugo's tone there was no way she could argue.

'Oh, Dad…' Emily closed her eyes, then crossed the room and touched her father lightly on the face. 'Then…' She looked down at him and her distress had almost completely gone. He had been a very old man, and with heart failure his death must have been expected. 'He died at peace?'

'He did,' Hugo said. 'I bet he wasn't even close to thinking about his dinner.'

'Thank you.' Emily turned a tearful face to Hugo, and then to Christie. 'Thank you both. I think you're both wonderful.'

'Which,' said Christie as the door closed behind them a short time later, 'is hardly fair because it wasn't me who granted her that peace of mind.'

'Forensic medicine's not your bag, then, Dr Flemming?'

Hugo's tone was slightly teasing as he limped beside her, and she cast him a confused sidelong glance.

'I know the steps of rigor mortis but as for the timing of temperature changes…were you sure in there, or were you making it up?'

He grinned. 'Oh, ye of little faith.'

'You're saying always trust a specialist.' Her lips curved in response. 'How can I doubt such an oracle? But…'

'But?'

'But what call does an anaesthetist have for such knowledge?'

'I do a nice murder in my spare time.'

'Oh, right.' She chuckled, the tension and sadness of the scene they were leaving dissipating in the warm night air. 'So it's murder, sailing and a spot of anaesthetics on the side. You're quite a doctor, Dr Tallent.'

'I am, that.'

'And modest to boot?'

'I'm famed for my modesty,' he told her, casting down his eyes in demure and humble pose. 'Brilliant, brave, strong, humble…'

'Quite a guy, in fact.'

'I thought you'd never notice.' His free hand came out and took hers, and suddenly she was almost breathless. They'd reached the car, and stopped. Hugo still leaned on his walking stick, and in Christie's free hand she held her doctor's bag, but by their two free hands they were linked.

And by something else…

'Thank you anyway,' she said awkwardly, her laughter fading. 'What you did for Emily in there…'

'It was nothing.'

'She'd have agonised for the rest of her life if she thought her father died angry. She's been a wonderful daughter to a very difficult old man, and I don't mind if what you said wasn't true.'

'Hey, it was true,' he said, wounded.

'Even if it wasn't,' she went on with determination, 'it was wonderful.'

'Christie…'

'Mmm?'

'Shut up,' he said softly.

'Why would I shut up?'

'Because I'm going to kiss you,' he said—and proceeded to do just that.

Love-making aside, Christie had to check her patients in the hospital. Nine-year-old Mary Adams was still tight with asthma. The child really needed specialist attention and treatment but her parents refused to take her off the island—and there was no way Christie would let Hugo take her load that night.

'Go and make yourself a cup of cocoa and go to bed,' she told him as she half pushed him out of the car. Heavens, the man was incorrigible. He'd kissed her for a full five minutes in front of Don Parker's house, and if the undertaker hadn't pulled up behind them it was Christie's belief that she would still be there, being kissed.

And if she just moved sideways now…

Ridiculous. It was crazy to feel like this—like her body was on fire with warmth and wanting and…life. It was as if she'd been dormant for years, and things were happening now that had been suppressed for far too long.

Well, maybe they had, but in three more days they'd be suppressed for life so they may as well get used to it now.

'Please,' she said to Hugo. 'You're supposed to be an invalid. Your knee must be hurting—plus you must still be recovering from that bang on the head. I don't know what I was about, letting you stay up this late.'

'No, Dr Flemming?' He smiled at her—and what a

smile! It suggested all sorts of things she barely recognised—and yet she knew they were true.

'No,' she managed. 'Hugo…be sensible. Go to bed.' Her voice was suddenly breathless—as if she was on the edge of something she didn't understand in the least—and then she felt angry with herself at the jab of regret she experienced as he nodded.

'OK, Florence, my love. You win.' His smile slipped a little and she could suddenly see weariness in his expression. Maybe he wasn't quite as invincible as he thought.

'Off you go with your lamp of healing,' he told her, and he leaned over and touched her lips—a feather touch—a touch which shouldn't have had the effect of sending a zillion volts of electricity straight through her but did just that. Even more than the intense embrace they'd just enjoyed. 'Into the fray…'

He climbed from the car and then stood and watched her go. He watched until the taillights of her car disappeared around the bend toward the hospital.

And his face was suddenly impassive.

Christie had just meant to check Mary—after all, the little girl was the only one of her patients who was unstable and it was close to midnight—but in the end old Mr Handell was awake and complaining of pain in his hip. She needed to increase his morphine and go over for the hundredth time why he really needed to get himself an artificial hip and why she couldn't do such an operation on the island. He was only hospitalised because of immobility. If she could make him see the sense of a simple operation…

Some things were impossible. Especially at midnight.

Then she chatted to the night sister for half an hour. Eileen was agog with island news, and she also wanted to talk through a couple of patient worries. If Christie didn't do it now she'd need to rise at six to do it, she thought wearily, a time when Eileen would be at her busiest.

So she managed to hold back her reluctance to head back to the cottage—and Hugo—and do what was needed.

Then, just as she was about to leave, Eileen said, 'Young David Myers is due for his feed. Would you like to take him to his mother?'

Sigh...

But Eileen knew Christie and Liz Myers were friends. There was no reason in the wide world why Christie shouldn't take the baby from the nursery and wake his mother.

Except that Hugo was waiting.

If she said that, wouldn't that set the whole island talking? Good grief! So Christie managed a smile, checked the small but wailing David—the infant was doing fantastically well for a premmie—and wheeled him down the corridor to Liz.

She didn't need to wake Liz. Liz was wide awake and waiting for him.

'Christie.' Her eyes lit at the sight of her friend.

First things first, though. Young David wasn't interested in social niceties. His mother hitched herself up in bed, wincing from post-operative twinges, and settled her son onto her breast. David latched on like a leech, cast a fearful glance upward as if to say, Any ideas of disengaging me and I'm ready to yell the place down, and blissful silence reigned.

Lovely. And now maybe Christie could escape.

'I only popped in on my way home,' Christie said apologetically. 'Eileen will take him back when he's finished.' Then, because she must, she added a rider. 'Any problems, Liz?'

'Yes,' Liz said mournfully. 'About a million. Every time I move.'

'You're doing really well,' Christie said encouragingly. 'I know it hurts like crazy, but it'll settle, and at least—'

'At least I don't have haemorrhoids from pushing,' Liz finished for her. 'If that was what you were going to say then I'm not interested. I have my own ouches and that's all I'm interested in, thank you very much.'

'I wasn't, actually,' Christie told her, smiling. 'It was just—'

'I know, I know.' Liz cuddled her little one close and smiled. 'I should count my blessings. And, of course, I am. You can't doubt that I have been. I knew all about the risks of Caesarean under general anaesthetic. When you said you'd do it under a general, I thought I'd lost my baby.'

'Liz!'

'Well, I did.' She gave a shamefaced grin. 'I can tell you now, I spent my entire pregnancy expecting something dreadful to go wrong. I ordered medical books over the internet, you see. I became a sort of modern-day compulsive doomsayer. You name it, I imagined it. Or I found a picture of it in a textbook. I had pictures of babies with two heads, babies with no heads at all, babies with gene abnormalities, Siamese twins, Siamese triplets even…'

'You didn't tell me,' Christie said faintly.

'You would have told me I was being ridiculous,' Liz told her. 'Which I was. Especially after I had a scan and they actually head-counted. It was just that I didn't believe them.' She smiled down at her little one, and there was pure joy in her eyes. 'Not until now. I didn't believe I could end up with such a perfect baby, you see. And then, when I went into labour and you said you'd do a general, it was just what I'd expected…'

'Oh, Liz…'

'I knew the anaesthetic would cross the placenta,' Liz said. 'I knew my baby would be dead. And now he's not. Thanks to Hugo.'

Thanks to Hugo... 'Thanks very much,' Christie said with token terseness. She was feeling ill at the thought of her friend worrying so much—and she hadn't guessed—but even so, hey, some credit for a healthy baby should surely come her way. Even though Hugo had done a great job! 'There have been heaps of successful deliveries of babies under general anaesthetic.'

'Are you telling me I shouldn't think Hugo Tallent is wonderful?' Liz demanded.

'He thinks that all by himself,' Christie said shortly. 'There's no need to build the man's ego up any more than it is.'

'And you don't think he's wonderful?'

'I...'

'Christie!' Liz's eyes were suddenly intent. She still held her baby close but her attention was diverted. She knew Christie very well indeed. 'Christie Flemming...'

'I need to go,' Christie said shortly, fighting mounting colour.

'You think he's wonderful, too,' Liz said on a long note of discovery. 'Well, well.'

'Well, well, what?' Christie glowered. 'And what if I do? The man's a city specialist. Of course he's Mr Wonderful. But he has nothing to do with me.'

'You could be a city doctor,' Liz said, hurling herself straight into a happy ending. 'You could finish training in surgery and—'

'Oh, right. Sure. And leave the island without a doctor? Force Grandpa to leave the island or have him face old age alone? I don't think so.'

Liz grimaced as her fairy-tale dissipated. 'I guess not. It just seems so unfair,' she said slowly, sinking back onto her pillows and relaxing as her baby sucked on. 'That you do without a love life for us...'

'I'm not being offered a love life,' Christie snapped. 'Just because the man kissed me...'

'He kissed you?' Liz sat up again. Her stitches pulled, she gave a yelp and young David gave an angry whimper. He was a baby who didn't like his mealtimes disturbed. 'Whoops, sorry, love,' his mum said contritely, but she was still on track. She resettled her son and then fixed her friend with a look that said *Tell all or else! 'Hugo Tallent kissed you?'*

'You want to tell the whole hospital?' Holy heck, Liz's astonished squeak could be heard the length of the corridor.

'I don't mind. Seriously? He kissed you?'

'Yes, but...'

'Yes, but what?'

'How many men kissed you before you married your Henry?' Christie demanded, and Liz looked disconcerted.

'I don't know, but—'

'You lost count?'

'Maybe, but—'

'But what? What's the difference?' Christie demanded. 'A kiss doesn't necessarily imply long-term commitment. Why does it have to have to mean anything different if a man kisses me?'

'I'm not the island doctor,' Liz told her bluntly. 'If someone kisses you—'

'They mean business. Yeah, right. But not now. If an islander kisses me he knows he's making a huge statement—because of who I am. But Hugo is just like the men I met when I was at medical school. He can kiss me, you see, and then walk away. There's not this whole huge expectation thing...'

'Except that your heart isn't untouched,' Liz whispered softly, watching her friend's face. 'Is it?'

'Of course it is.' Christie flushed. 'Untouched, I mean. It meant nothing.'

'Nope.' Liz reached out and touched Christie lightly on the cheek. 'Oh, my dear, be careful. If you really don't think there's a future don't let yourself fall any further.'

Which was fine advice, Christie thought crossly as she parked her car and made her way into the cottage, but how did one make one's heart follow the advice of one's head. She could tell herself very sensibly that she was mad to even let herself think about the way Hugo felt. The touch of his mouth on hers... The way his eyes held her and caressed her from across the room...

She could tell herself it was nonsense to do anything but put it straight out of her mind and get on with her medicine.

So why did her heart lurch as she opened the front door? Because Hugo was inside.

He was in bed.

Of course he was, and it was stupid to feel a stab of disappointment that he was. His door was firmly closed and there was no chink of light underneath.

What else had she expected? Christie asked herself crossly. He'd had a fun night prawning, he'd kissed her once on the beach, things had become emotional with the old man's death and he'd kissed her a second time.

That was it. End of story.

As soon as this wind eased he'd be off the island, she told herself, and she'd never need to see him again. And she'd go on being Briman Island's doctor. For ever.

For ever was a very long time.

There was a pad on the kitchen bench. More of Hugo's handwriting. She was starting to recognise it now, and she picked the pad up idly and stared at it. And then stared some more.

This was curiouser and curiouser.

Here was her prawn escapade, set down in as much detail as Scrubbit-the-dog's operation had been. Every last detail was recorded, and it was as detailed as a photograph. He hadn't left out anything.

Except the kiss.

He'd stopped at the prawns. Peeling the prawns…the taste of them. The smell. The firelight and the sun-warmed sand.

And then merciful blankness.

Not a spy. But…what?

Hugo wasn't asleep.

He lay in the spare bedroom, his arms linked behind his head and stared up at the darkened ceiling. He heard Christie come in, he heard her pause by his door and then he heard her silence.

Damn, he'd left his notes on the bench, he thought suddenly as he heard the faint rustle of paper and realised she was reading them. She'd think he was nuts. Still, he wasn't going to charge out now, because he knew that once he saw her… Once he saw her…

That way lay disaster!

Disaster?

Yes!

He didn't want this, he told himself. It must be the knock on the head that was telling him he wanted to get involved. His life was busy beyond belief. Crazy. He was way behind schedule now—he'd never planned to take a week off for a yachting expedition. He was expected back in Brisbane on Saturday, he was due in New York on Monday and then back at the hospital the following week.

He'd meant to spend the time on the yacht, sorting things out, and now all he'd done had been to get himself more confused. Hell, the whole next chapter was a nightmare. A jumble of ideas that wouldn't gel.

Harry would have to take over from him in Brisbane. He was good enough as an anaesthetist—he could handle an extra week's work while Hugo did what he needed to in New York.

And where did Christie fit into all this?

She didn't, he told himself ruthlessly. Women? Huh! He'd had enough of women and then some. Since his mother had died women were an expendable item in Hugo's life. They had to be. There simply wasn't room to fit one in around the edges.

But Christie was different.

Different? Christie was impossible!

CHAPTER SEVEN

CHRISTIE didn't see Hugo again until the next night.

The islanders must have saved their combined ills until today, she thought wearily, pushing her curls back from her face and taking the last file out to Reception. She'd had one crisis after another. She needed to spend Wednesday at the Koori settlement on the other end of the island, so it was no use trying to shelve work until tomorrow. It had to be done now.

So she worked as she normally did—hard. She left the cottage before either Stan or Hugo woke, she hadn't had time for lunch and now she was late for dinner.

There'd been no time for shopping. It'd have to be eggs on toast, she thought bleakly. Hugo could like it or lump it. It'd be a bit different from last night's feast but it would have to do.

At least the wind was dying. Christie came out of the surgery and faced what had been a force ten gale. She found it was still blowing rough but it was definitely easing.

'Heading home to your Hugo?' Ray, the practice secretary, grinned as he came out and locked up after her. 'Can we get rid of Dr Stan again tonight?'

How many of the islanders knew she'd spent last night with Hugo? she wondered. Most of them, at a guess.

'Why would I want to get rid of Grandpa?'

Ray smiled. He was an ex-fisherman who'd lost a hand, setting nets. He'd turned into the doctors' receptionist twenty years back and he now ruled the practice as if it was personally his.

'You deserve a bit of a love life, girl,' he said softly. 'It's a hard slog by yourself.'

Oh, for heaven's sake… 'This hardly has the potential for a love life,' she retorted. 'No matter how much the gossipmongers want it to be. He's heading home to Brisbane just as soon as the wind dies.'

'Is he?' Ray's eyebrows arched and Christie paused. She knew Ray well enough by now to know when he was big with news.

'What do you know that I don't?' she demanded.

'Idle gossip,' he said—and grinned again. And so did she.

'Go on, then. Out with it. Passing on idle gossip is included in your job description. You know I can't practise medicine on this island without it.'

She couldn't either. The number of times she'd just 'happened' to drop by when someone had been in trouble—because of what Ray had told her—was beyond counting.

'It's just that the mainland plane's preparing to return to the island on Thursday,' Ray said. 'The weather forecast says this lot of weather'll have passed by then. Your Dr Tallent saw Lisa at the booking office this morning but, instead of buying a ticket for him to head home, it seems he's bought another ticket for someone else to come here.'

'Someone else?'

'That's all I know,' Ray said, holding his hands up to show they were empty of any more information. 'Me, I know nothing.' The grin flashed out again. 'Mind, it's not for want of trying. He's bought an adult return ticket in the name of Tallent, and that's all I know. That's all Lisa knows. It could be for anyone.'

So, if he was bringing someone else here…

Hmm. Where did he intend putting up this bearer of an 'adult return ticket in the name of Tallent'?

The guest bed was a double, but he couldn't assume that someone else could stay in Grandpa's cottage, Christie thought. It wasn't exactly a huge double bed. Whoever shared it would have to be close.

Good grief, maybe he *was* married!

Maybe she shouldn't care.

'Don't get your knickers in a knot,' Christie told herself, stomping up the track to the cottage. It was hard work against the wind but she didn't care—in fact, she almost relished it. It gave her frustration an outlet. 'You know nothing.

'He could have told me what he planned.' She was talking to herself into the wind. If anyone saw her they'd assume she was nuts, but it was seven at night, the islanders were at their dinner and the windswept track was safely deserted.

She was free to talk to herself as much as she liked. So…

'He's hardly seen you,' she reminded herself. 'He'll have told Grandpa that he's bringing someone else, and of course, Grandpa will have agreed. An extra visitor? he'll think. Great! So Dr Tallent will be sitting in my kitchen, waiting for me to come and feed him, discussing this extra visitor with Grandpa. And where am I going to find the money out of housekeeping? Drat the man!

'If it's a woman…

'Oh, for heaven's sake.' She gave herself an angry shake. This was nothing to do with her. And maybe Ray had it wrong—or maybe the return ticket was for a mainland boat-builder to assess his boat, she thought suddenly, and Lisa might have forgotten to mention the extra single ticket he'd bought for himself.

That made sense, she decided. It *must* be a boat-builder. Hugo wouldn't entrust his father's precious yacht to island carpenters. He'd organise its repair and then he'd be leaving.

Good! she told herself bitterly. Life could then get back to normal!

Hugo *was* still in her kitchen, but he wasn't waiting to be fed. Christie opened the door, took one sniff and knew this was something special. There was the rich aroma of different herbs, amazing herbs—herbs she'd never smelled before. It smelled like...

'Curry,' she said faintly before the door was fully open. 'There's a curry in my kitchen!'

'Well guessed.' Hugo was standing by the stove. He turned to greet her and his smile enveloped all of her, from the tip of her toes to her flushed-from-the-wind cheeks. 'Great detective work, Dr Flemming. What sort?'

'What sort of curry?' She stopped dead and blinked in astonishment. Grandpa was sitting at the kitchen table, chopping something green she didn't recognise. The old doctor smiled a welcome at her and then went back to chopping, his good hand working with surgical precision.

Grandpa? *Cooking!*

'You can't get more than one sort of curry on this island,' she said cautiously, taking in the scene before her in disbelief. 'Curry curry?'

'Curry curry!' Hugo gave a snort of derision and went back to stirring. 'For heaven's sake! Don't you frequent curry-houses? Anyone would think you live on a tropical island, Dr Flemming.'

'Anyone would be right,' she retorted. 'A tropical island ruled by Doris the store-keeper. Doris's sole curry ingredient is no-name-curry-powder, as she says any other type contains garlic. Which makes one unsociable.'

'Only to non-garlic eaters.' Hugo grinned. 'So you and I and Stan are all going to eat garlic tonight. Heaps and heaps of garlic.'

She put her hands on her hips, trying not to laugh. 'And what about my patients tomorrow?'

'Tell 'em if they don't like your garlic then they can find themselves another doctor,' Hugo told her firmly. 'But I wouldn't worry. By now most of the island knows what we're eating.'

'Most…'

'We had an ingredient hunt,' Stan told her. By the look on his face he was enjoying himself hugely. 'Hugo decided he'd like to cook a curry, so we downloaded recipes from the internet and then went on a curry hunt.'

'Your grandpa knows what's in every islander's back yard,' Hugo told her. Honestly, they were like two kids with a new toy, desperate to show it off. If they'd had tails, they'd both have been wagging them!

'Phyllis Hay grows garlic to protect her roses from aphids,' Stan interjected. 'Mary and Bob Harvey have been boasting about their herb garden for years—not that they ever use any—so we got a heap from them. Including this coriander.' He held a piece high—a feathery green frond with root attached. 'Look at this. It smells so much even I can get a whiff, and my nose has hardly been working since the stroke. And old Tom Bangarrana grows ginger and chilis.'

'You've been planning dinner all day,' Christie said, stunned, but Hugo shook his head.

'Nope. This morning Stan and I went all over the boat, figuring out what had to be done.'

'Yeah, right.' *Stan and I…* As if Grandpa could crawl all over a damaged boat.

But Stan hadn't been idle. 'I introduced Hugo to the best boat-builder on the island,' Stan told her. 'Old Alf Willis is just aching to get his hands on it.'

Christie frowned, taking this in. 'I'd forgotten Alf was a boat-builder.'

'Most people have,' Stan said sadly. 'The fishermen ge those modern fibreglass hulls from the mainland now. Bu *Sandpiper* is timber-hulled. She's a beautiful piece o work—or she will be when Alf gets his hands on her.'

'You'd trust your boat to Alf?' she asked, and Hug raised his brows.

'Shouldn't I?'

'I suppose so.' She was having trouble taking this o board, but the more she thought about it the more delighte she felt. Alf was an elderly man with a nagging wife an almost terminal depression. She couldn't think of a bette tonic for him than the repair of a beautiful boat.

'My father's flying in on Thursday to make the fina decision,' Hugo told her. 'But I think it'll work out reall well.'

'Oh.' So that was the extra ticket. His father... She trie to glower. 'So where's he staying?'

'Next door. I've rented it.'

That set her back. She stared and Hugo chuckled.

'Oh, dear. You weren't getting your knickers in a kno about me landing extra people on you, were you, D Flemming?'

'I... No.' But it was exactly what she'd thought. Sh couldn't stop her colour rising.

And he saw. This man could read her mind!

'Dear, dear. All that spleen vented for nothing.'

'I did not vent my spleen!'

'I watched you come up the path.' He motioned to th window. 'You were venting your spleen like anything. bet someone told you my father was coming and you pu two and two together and felt put upon.'

'I didn't.'

'You did.' He smiled then, the lazy, gentle smile tha had her heart doing handsprings. 'I guess I should hav warned you. The whole island puts upon you. You wouldn't know that I'd be any different.'

He took her breath away. He just had to stand—and look—and she couldn't think of a single thing to say. Different! Of course he was different. He was…Hugo!

'I…' She finally found her voice, but it was with a huge effort and both men were watching her. Hugo with sympathy. Stan with blatant curiosity. He hadn't seen his granddaughter act like this before. Her face was colouring and fading like traffic lights.

'Are you and your father both staying next door?' she asked, and tried hard to sound like it wasn't important.

'I'll just stay to settle Dad in,' he said. His expression tightened. He had a way of stopping questions in their tracks, did Hugo Tallent, and she couldn't go further. After all, it was none of her business—was it?

'How… how on earth did you rent next door?' she finally managed.

'You know it's been empty since Doris's folks died,' Stan told her, still eyeing his granddaughter with speculative interest. 'She hates the thought of selling it, but it's still furnished, and the thought of Dr Tallent's dad staying here…'

'She's never agreed!'

'Our Hugo oozes charm when he wants something.' Stan chuckled. 'You should have seen him. You'd have thought Doris was twenty-five instead of sixty, and she was blushing like a schoolgirl as she agreed to give the place a dust and make up the beds.' He chuckled again. 'You watch it, miss,' he warned his granddaughter. 'What Hugo wants, Hugo gets. Now, about this curry…'

The curry was wonderful, but anything would have tasted wonderful tonight. When was the last time someone had cooked for her? Christie thought. Not since she'd come to the island. The sensation was so novel that bread and drip-

ping would have tasted great. As it was, the curry was
fantastic, as was the fragrant rice and the chapatis and the
dhal that went with it.

And the company...

'Marry me,' she said as she ate her last mouthful. She
looked over the table at Hugo and she smiled. 'Marry me
immediately. I've died and gone to heaven.'

It had been meant flippantly. Sort of. It had been meant
as a joke.

But Hugo didn't smile. Instead, the laughter behind his
eyes faded and the look he gave her made a tremor run
straight down her spine.

'There's a few things we need to work on yet, love
before we go down that road,' he told her gently, and then
as she gasped and stared, he shook his head.

'Give it time, Christie, love. Give us all time.'

What could she say after that? Nothing, she thought. It
was best ignored. It had been a flippant comment on her
part—hadn't it? And it must surely have been the same on
his. She cleared the table, she washed and Hugo wiped, and
Hugo and Stan chatted, but she stayed silent. She was
weary but it wasn't weariness that was holding her tongue

Finally she could stand it no longer. How the men could
simply chat while there was so much tension in the room
she didn't know...

There were still things to be done. She had to get out of
the cottage right now.

'I'll leave you for a bit,' she told them, cutting across
their conversation in a way that was almost rude. In truth,
she'd barely registered what they were talking about.

Hugo stopped talking and raised his eyebrows. 'You
need to go out again?'

'I promised Mandy I'd take Scrubbit home,' she said
'Mandy's parents won't bring the car out to take a dog

ome, and I don't want her carrying him that far. He's best
not jolted.'

She hesitated and forced herself to meet Hugo's eyes.
There was something that needed to be said, and this wasn't
about her. He looked gravely questioning. The laughter
seemed to have gone.

'I…I assume you've talked to Mandy's parents. About
what you promised?'

'I tried today but they weren't in.' Hugo turned to Stan.
'So I guess this is a good opportunity. If you'll excuse me,
I'll go with Christie.'

'You do that, boy.' Once again Stan chuckled. 'And take
your time,' he added. 'If you park on the headland, you
can see all over the estuary. It's where I used to take
Christie's grandmother, and it's a very useful spot.'

'For what, sir?' Hugo couldn't help himself, Christie
thought as laughter sprang back into his eyes. Honestly, the
man was incorrigible.

'If you don't know by now, then I'm not the man to be
telling you,' Stan retorted. 'Nor are you the man I think
you are, Hugo Tallent. Now, get out of here, the pair of
you, and leave an old man to remember what the headland
could be on a night like this.'

Whoa…

Christie's face was burning so fiercely that she didn't
know where to put herself. Instead, she retired into silence.

As did Hugo. He gave her one sideways glance as he
slid into the passenger seat beside her, and then retreated
into silence himself.

There were all sorts of things happening in that silence,
and Christie didn't understand any of them.

Scrubbit was waiting for them. He gave a healthy bark as
they entered the animal surgery, and Christie grimaced.

She'd checked him a couple of hours back but things ha[d] changed.

'I might have known. You've pulled the drip out, yo[u] dopey animal.' She crossed to his cage and scooped hi[m] into her arms. 'Let's look at you.'

The little dog looked up at her, and his stumpy ta[il] started spinning like a propeller. He'd obviously dispense[d] with his drip, but by the speed of his motor Christie coul[d] tell he no longer needed it.

'This is one amazing pooch,' Hugo said, looking dow[n] at the creature in Christie's arms. 'You wouldn't see m[e] pulling a drip out after an operation like that.'

'Or working as an anaesthetist the day after sufferin[g] respiratory arrest. You wouldn't do that either, now, woul[d] you?' Christie managed a grin. 'You're two of a kind, Hug[o] Tallent. You and one dopey mutt.'

'Gee, thanks.'

And then there was silence. There were a thousand thing[s] to say, but it was unsafe to say any of them.

Gloria and Barry King were home. Christie could hear the[ir] television from the road, and upstairs Mandy's light shon[e] from her attic bedroom. With such a promise before he[r] and exams in two weeks, there was no doubt where she'[d] be.

'Here goes,' Christie said ruefully as they walked up th[e] path. She wrinkled her nose and Hugo looked a question.

'That bad?'

'And then some. You wait and see.'

There was no time for more. Christie knocked whil[e] Hugo held the dog. There was the sound of an angry femal[e] voice, and a man's disclaiming knowledge of visitors[.] Christie knocked again, and waited. She was accustome[d] to Gloria.

She looked wary, Hugo thought as he watched her. Thi[s]

Gloria woman seemed to have put the wind up the entire island. What on earth was she on about?

He reached out and took Christie's hand, and his smile enveloped her.

'Courage, love,' he said. 'I'm not letting you face dragons alone.'

And it was odd, but Christie gave him a look that said maybe it wasn't Gloria she was afraid of.

Finally Gloria opened the door. The woman was wearing night attire, and Hugo knew his lingerie. Her satin dressing-gown would have cost a mint and she was tottering on ridiculous slippers which must have cost as much. Gloria was a hard-faced, cold-eyed platinum blonde. She saw Christie first—and then she saw Scrubbit.

'I told Mandy to have *that* put down,' she said flatly. 'We don't want it.' And she started to close the door.

Hugo's boot came out and wedged itself between door and frame. If he'd been wearing his borrowed yachting casuals, Gloria would have broken his toe. As it was, leather-booted and protected, he still had to bite back a yelp.

He managed. It was undignified to yelp in the face of hostility, he decided. He was here on a mission, and he'd been warned.

Dragon-slayers didn't yelp.

'May we come in?' he asked politely.

Gloria hauled the door wide and then proceeded to try and slam it shut. She didn't make it. With one deft movement Hugo stepped in, stopped the door in its swing and leaned against it so that Christie could follow.

'Good evening, Mrs King,' Hugo said smoothly, as if he hadn't noticed anything unwelcoming. 'I'm Dr Tallent. I've been assisting Dr Flemming in the care of your daughter's dog.'

But Gloria wasn't looking at him. She was staring down

at the dressing on Scrubbit's leg and she looked appalled. The dog had obviously had medical attention!

'We're not paying,' she snapped. 'I told Barry he had to put it down. *Barry!*' Her screech was enough to waken the dead. 'I thought I told you to put the mutt down.'

'*Scrubbit!*'

The cry was from Mandy. She'd emerged from her bedroom upstairs and now came tumbling down to scoop the little dog into her arms. 'Scrubbit, you're home.' She turned shining eyes to Christie. 'Oh, he looks great. Thank you. Thank you, thank you, thank you.'

'We're not paying.' Gloria's voice was still sharp. 'You needn't think you'll get a cent from us.'

'I'm not charging,' Christie said wearily. 'I like Scrubbit, and Mandy is my friend. Maybe after her exams she can spend time sorting files for me as payment.'

'Fat chance,' Gloria snapped. 'She'll be getting a full-time job after her exams. I've had enough of this school garbage.'

As Gloria spoke, her husband had emerged from the living room, but he said nothing. Barry King stood silent, scrawny and unhappy, looking as if he was trying desperately to melt into the woodwork.

'It's odd you should mention schooling, but that's why I'm here, Mrs King,' Hugo said easily. He looked behind her to her husband. 'Is it OK if we come in for a minute?'

'No!' Gloria's voice was an icy spit.

But Hugo wasn't talking to Gloria. 'Mr King?' His eyes rested on Barry's—man to man—and Barry shifted uneasily. 'May we come in?'

'No…'

'Mr King?' Hugo simply ignored the vitriolic woman. He was waiting for Barry's response. Barry shifted again, but Hugo's eyes didn't let him off the hook.

'I need to talk to you,' he said gently. 'May I do that?'

And with Hugo's eyes boring straight into his, there was little else the man could say.

'Yeah, sure,' he stuttered. 'I… I guess…'

'Thank you.' Hugo needed no second invitation. He strode into the living room, flicked off the television and sank into the largest armchair—as if he meant to stay for a while. It was almost as if this were his home. 'Mandy, take Scrubbit up to your room,' he told the open-mouthed girl. 'This discussion is between Dr Flemming, your parents and me.'

'But…'

'Hop it, love,' he told her. He winked at her and then patted the chair beside him. 'Christie, you sit here. Mrs King, Mr King…make yourselves comfortable. I have a few things I need to run through with you.'

Christie could only boggle. In thirty swift seconds he'd turned the tables completely. It wasn't Gloria who was in charge now; it was Hugo, and all Gloria could do was gape. Hugo smiled at them politely and waited for them to sit. To Christie's astonishment, they sat.

'You have a very bright daughter,' Hugo told them. He raised his brows and waited for Gloria's reaction.

He got it. 'She thinks she is.' Gloria was off balance but she was still vicious. 'She's no better than any other island kid. She has fancy ideas—'

'Her teacher says she'll get excellent marks. Fantastic marks, in fact.'

'So what?'

Hugo leaned forward. He linked his hands together and regarded both of them—first Barry, then Gloria and then Barry again. His gaze stayed fixed on Barry.

'Mandy loves animals,' he said gently. 'I've watched her working. Your daughter has the ability to be an excellent veterinary surgeon.'

'It's out of the question—' Gloria started, but she wa~
ignored.

'If she had the money to go to university,' Hugo kep
on, his eyes still on Barry, 'would you stop her going?'

'I…' The hapless man started to turn to Gloria bu
Hugo's voice dragged his attention back to him.

'Mr King, I'm speaking to *you*. If your daughter had th
funds to do veterinary science, would you prevent her?'

Barry took a deep breath. He cast a fearful look at hi~
wife, then turned back to Hugo.

'N-no,' he said, and it sounded as if it had taken all hi~
courage to say it. 'I wouldn't. She's a good kid. But there'
no way—'

'I'll supply the funds.'

Silence. You could have heard a pin drop. What Christi~
did hear was Mandy's heavy breathing as she listened o~
the other side of the door.

Hugo had them all in the palm of his hand, and Christi~
found herself almost scared to breathe. What he was doin~
was stunning.

At last the silence broke and, predictably, it was broke~
by Gloria. 'What are you talking about?' she snapped. 'Sh~
can't afford to go to Brisbane. A vet course takes five years
Five years without any pay. Without—'

'I'm paying,' Hugo said flatly. 'Your daughter has a rea~
love for animals and she has a gift for healing. Anyone ca~
see that. All I'm doing is providing the funds to let her d~
it.'

The woman's eyes narrowed. 'Yes? Give us the money
then,' she said quickly. 'We'll see she uses it properly.'

'I can't do that.' Hugo smiled and looked across a
Christie. 'Dr Flemming doesn't trust me, you see,' he sai~
apologetically. 'She wants guarantees before Mandy start~
her course, so I'll put the money into a trust account. Th~

ustees will administer it as she needs it and, as from now,
he'll cease costing you a cent.'

Gloria was *almost* speechless. 'But what's in it for you?'

'The knowledge that in five years Briman Island may
vell have a vet.' Hugo's smile slipped and he looked across
t Barry as if he expected him to understand. 'And as well
s that, you know I had a very close shave with death the
ther day. You were one of the fishermen who brought your
oat out to rescue me. This is part of my way of saying
hank you.'

'I—I can't believe you'll do this—for our kid,' Barry
tammered, but Gloria wasn't done. She was practically
ibbering.

'She's not taking it. She's getting a job. I want her wages
o help pay her keep.'

She might have known. Of course, Christie thought.
Gloria had expensive tastes. She wasn't happy with what
Barry earned and she'd have designs on what little Mandy
ould contribute. Christie grimaced in distaste, but Hugo
lidn't signify even by a look that he understood what
Gloria meant.

'She won't need keep,' he said gently. He still looked at
Barry. 'She'll be living in Brisbane at my expense. Will
ou let your daughter have this chance, Mr King? What do
ou say?'

All eyes were now on Barry. Even Gloria's.

And, amazingly, he rose to the occasion. For once in his
ife, he made a stand. Barry's wobbly chin firmed. His
houlders went back, and for the first time he looked at his
wife with a trace of sternness. He held her gaze for a long,
ong moment, and then he turned to Hugo.

'Yes,' he told him. 'Yes, she'll have this chance. She'll
accept with pleasure.'

'No! I'll kill the dog,' Gloria screeched, rising to her feet.
'I'll—'

'Sit down and shut up, Gloria,' Barry said. 'From her
on in you just shut up. If Mandy doesn't want to take he
dog to Brisbane then I'll take care of it myself. If you mes
things up for Mandy, she won't ever want to come home
She won't want anything to do with us. And that's the las
straw. So you can shut your trap and say thank you to D
Tallent. And you'll wish your daughter well…'

Gloria was left with nothing to say. Barry fussed aroun
and made tea, and called Mandy downstairs—or from be
hind her door—and teased her about her good fortune
while all the time Gloria sat grim-faced and silent. Sh
seemed to have had all the puff taken out of her.

What would happen here when they left? Christie won
dered, and found herself worrying. It was all very well t
give this gift to Mandy, but to destroy the family in th
process…

This was what being a general practitioner was all about
she thought bitterly. What Hugo didn't understand. In
community like this, you never treated one problem in iso
lation. You treated the whole picture.

She looked at Barry, and found herself wondering wha
was in store for him now. Years with a shrew for a wife—
or would Gloria be so angry she'd leave?

But she'd underestimated Hugo. Of course, Christie real
ised as she watched his thoughtful eyes resting on Mandy'
mother. He was wondering exactly the same as she was.

Of course he was. They had like minds…

And the thought suddenly made her feel almost physi
cally ill. This man seemed like the other half to her whole
and she hadn't known the half was missing until she'd me
him. But now she knew what it was to love—and it wa
useless! She wanted him so much, she thought, and th
aching need was threatening to overwhelm her.

All she could do was watch and listen—and hunger fo
what might have been…

And Hugo was unaware. He was still focussed on Gloria. Finishing his tea, he walked forward and stooped before Gloria's drooping figure.

'This'll be fine, Gloria,' he said softly, taking her hands. 'A daughter as a vet is a thing to be proud of. I'll bet there's no other woman on this island who could boast of that.'

Gloria looked up, her face frozen.

'And it won't cost you a cent. A vet in the family for nothing... She'll earn fine wages.'

And there was one last thing...

'Gloria, why are you limping?' he asked, and the woman's breath hissed in.

'I'm not.'

'I watched you.' She was wearing high-heeled fluffy slippers. Her feet were out in front of her now and Hugo looked down at them. 'Do you have a painful foot? You're walking like it's been hurting for a while. Your hip is dropping like you're used to carrying it.'

Christie frowned. Gloria limping? Was she? She should have noticed that.

Then she thought back. Gloria had always limped, she thought suddenly. Ever since she'd known her. She'd always worn ridiculously high shoes—maybe Christie had always assumed that to be the cause.

'It's none of your business,' Gloria snapped, and Hugo nodded.

'That's right, it's not,' he agreed equitably. 'Your daughter's education isn't my business either, but I'm sticking my oar in there so I might as well stick it in elsewhere.'

'Tell him about your feet, Mum,' Mandy piped up, and got a glare for her pains.

'You've never talked to me about sore feet,' Christie said wonderingly.

'I talked to your grandpa,' Gloria snapped. 'Years ago.

I even went to Townsville to see specialists. Fat lot of use they are. They can't do anything.'

'But your feet hurt.'

'Only the one,' she said grudgingly.

'What's the problem?' Suddenly Hugo was all doctor. He had a chameleon personality, Christie thought, changing at will. Ten minutes ago he'd acted as if he were made of iron. Now there was even tenderness in the way he talked to Gloria. To Gloria!

'I don't have to tell you…' Her voice fell away and Christie thought suddenly, She's ashamed!

'No.' Hugo nodded. 'You don't. But it's a free consultation I'm offering, and I'll be gone on Friday.'

Gone. Gone, Christie thought…

'I have papillomas,' Gloria said.

Hugo sat back and looked at her. 'Papillomas?'

'You must know what they are,' she jeered. 'They make my feet crack and swell and hurt—'

'I know what papillomas are. They're non-malignant tumours—like warts. But you've had them treated?'

'Of course I've had them treated,' she snapped. 'Years ago. I've had every treatment known to man. I had them cut off but they came back. I used this stinking ointment for years. I even had them blasted by this radiation treatment. Fat lot of good it did me. They just keep coming back and back and back. My foot's a mess.'

'May I see?' Hugo wasn't waiting for a response. He lifted her ridiculous pink slipper and slid it off her foot.

And Christie almost flinched at what she saw. She'd been trying to let her mind assimilate what she'd just learned for sure—*Hugo would be gone on Friday*. But now she was jerked back to medicine with a rush. Good grief!

The sole of Gloria's foot was a mass of papillomas. They covered almost all the ball of the foot, there were a couple between the toes and one huge one was on the heel. They were raised and ugly, one had cracked and looked infected, and they were in such a mass that they must have given her constant discomfort.

Gloria was bad-tempered at the best of times, and if she was in pain...

'Oh, Gloria, you should have said.' Christie frowned, thinking it through. Gloria hadn't consulted Christie in the time she'd been on the island, so she'd never checked her records. Stan had never said anything about this but he must have known.

This was a direct result of Gloria's nastiness, she thought. To enquire how Gloria was meant risking getting your head bitten off. So she never had.

'Fat lot of good it would have done if I'd said anything,' Gloria sneered at her across the room. 'Doctors can't help.'

'You know, I might just be able to.' Hugo was gently examining the foot.

'Oh, yeah. Where so many have failed?'

'There's a new treatment I've been reading about. If you let your daughter help...'

'Mandy?'

'That's the one,' he said cheerfully. 'The new healer in the family. What I'd like to do is treat you with dinitrochlorobenzene.'

'Dini... dinitrochlorobenzene.' She frowned. 'I've never heard of it.'

'I don't blame you. It's not the sort of thing Doris sells by the gallon drum.' Hugo sounded cheerful and confident—doctor in charge again. 'It's called DNCB for short. It's a substance that almost everyone becomes allergic to when it's applied to their skin. What we could do is use this allergic reaction to provoke your immune system.'

To Christie's surprise, Gloria's hostility seemed to be lessening. Her expression was curious, and also intelligent.

'Explain it to me,' she demanded, and Christie watched a Hugo did just that.

'Those papillomas have been on your foot for so long that your body doesn't know they're foreign any more,' he told her. 'Your body's not trying to get rid of them, so they're staying put. What I'd like to do, if you let me, is to pop a strong solution of DNCB on a spot on your arm.'

'And how's that going to help?' She was suspicious to the point of rudeness, but she was still acute and he had her total attention.

'In about three weeks you'll get an allergic reaction,' he told her. 'Your arm will be a bit itchy and red for a couple of days. But after that...'

'After that, what?' Christie was fascinated as well.

'After that I'll teach Mandy how to apply the solution to the centre of each of the affected parts of your foot. What will happen then is that your body will react to the papillomas as if it's allergic to them. It'll start shedding the skin around them, and eventually—hopefully—it'll scale off the papillomas themselves. It won't happen overnight, but in about three months I reckon we might get you clear.'

'Is that true?' She was almost speechless.

Christie thought, Just how much discomfort has she been putting up with?

'It's true.' Hugo looked up at her, and it was his very best doctor-to-patient smile. Trust me, the smile said, and who couldn't? It was the same smile that was capable of turning Christie's world on its ear. 'It's not a hundred per cent successful, but here, with such a mass, I'd be surprised if we didn't get very good results indeed.'

'If you can...'

'No promises, but let me try,' he told her. 'I'm going back to Brisbane on Friday. I'll send the DNCB straight back and Christie will get things under way.'

He was definitely going back. But not returning. What had he said? 'I'll send' not 'I'll bring'.

But Hugo wasn't finished yet. 'By the way, I'm starting to guess part of where Mandy got her brains,' he said, smiling so that no offence could be taken at his words. 'I guess it's no surprise. I hear she's brilliant, and academic excellence usually comes from parents.'

What was he talking about now? Christie was so confused that she just wanted to get out of there. She wanted to assimilate everything she'd just learned—including the fact that he was definitely leaving.

'You've taken in the DNCB explanation very quickly,' he told Gloria. 'Many people have trouble.'

'I used to be good at school,' Gloria said diffidently.

'She did, too,' Barry piped up, and there was still room for pride in his voice. For all her nastiness, there must still be affection there. 'Gloria was two years below me at school but the teachers put her up so she was working alongside me. She was doing year-ten work when she was supposed to be in year eight.'

'But there was nowhere to go after that?' Hugo asked.

Gloria's face was working. For one long moment, Christie thought she might be about to cry.

'I had to get a job,' she said at last. 'When I was fourteen Mum took me down to the cannery and that was it. *It!* The men could at least be fishermen. There was something for them. But not the women. Not if there wasn't enough money to send us away.'

'So you, too, had the brains to be a vet?'

'I guess.' And now there definitely were tears. The woman's hard shell had crumpled in the face of Hugo's pressure. 'But, thanks to you, Mandy'll get her chance.'

'Why don't you do something now?' Hugo asked, and the whole room held its breath.

'Like what? Education costs money and, in case you haven't noticed, I live on a dump of an island.'

'You have a television,' Hugo told her. 'There's distance education, which screens lectures at all sorts of times. Because you're mature and you live in a remote area, I'd be surprised if a degree course would cost you anything at all.'

'Yes?' Suspicion was once more written all over her face. 'What would I do?'

'Things like medicine are a bit hard to do via distance education,' Hugo admitted, smiling, 'but there are many other courses. What would you like to do?'

'I haven't thought.' She took a deep breath. 'The islanders would laugh.'

'Since when did you care about what the islanders think?' Hugo asked gently. 'Go on, Gloria. You could do all sorts of things. Literature. History. Creative writing maybe? Write the world's best detective thriller. Whatever—just give it a go. Study's great, and you'll be able to compare notes when Mandy comes home for holidays.'

'I…' She was staring at him, totally confused, and so was everyone else in the room. This was medicine at its best, Christie thought dazedly. A possible family cure, and not a pill in sight!

'Don't make a decision tonight,' he urged. 'I'll pick up an education catalogue in Brisbane and send it back with the DNCB.'

'Yes?' She flushed and glared, then rose and backed off a couple of paces. The old Gloria wasn't completely overwhelmed. 'I suppose you want me to say thank you.'

'I don't want anything of the kind,' Hugo told her. He smiled at Mandy and Barry, and he rubbed Scrubbit lightly behind his ear. The little dog was lying blissfully in Mandy's arms, clearly where he most wanted to be in the world. 'Bye, Scrubbit,' he said. 'Look after yourself, mate. Mandy, I'll be in touch about arrangements. Come on, Dr Flemming. There's more on our agenda tonight.'

'Exactly what sort of a doctor are you?'

By the time they reached Christie's car she was almost beside herself. She slid into the driver's seat, waited for Hugo and then let fly. 'I don't believe it,' she added before he could respond. 'First, you manipulate that family like you're a class-one conjuring act. Second, you notice Gloria's limp, and I practically grew up here and I hadn't noticed. Then you produce a miracle cure out of your magic hat—'

'It isn't a miracle cure and if you've been looking at Gloria's limp for years then it's no wonder you didn't see it.'

'Don't interrupt,' she said savagely. 'In one wave of your wand, you've given Gloria an interest that will hopefully take her mind off giving her family hell—it'll save that family from self-destruction if anything will. You know, I have Barry on antidepressants because of Gloria's vicious tongue, and if you've solved that—'

'I'm not expecting miracles.'

'It's a darn sight more helpful than Valium.' She shook her head in wonderment. 'You know about distance education. You know about DNCB, which is more than I do and I'm supposed to be a general practitioner. And you're a specialist! But you're not a dermatologist, and how you can keep up with dermatological literature as well as everything else when I don't have time to blink… Much less forensic medicine and psychology—plus the odd dog operation…' She ended up almost on a wail, and Hugo sat back and smirked.

'Feeling outclassed, Dr Flemming?'

'Yes,' she said bluntly. 'How much time do you spend on anaesthetics?'

'Plenty,' he said, wounded. 'Do you doubt my skills?'

'No, but—'

'Do you mind if we go down to the harbour?' he asked, glancing at his watch. 'I'm meeting someone down there.'

'You're meeting someone. At nine at night?'

'If you don't mind.'

'You're running my life,' she told him bitterly. 'Plus making me feel the most inferior doctor in Australia. You know that?'

'You are not an inferior doctor,' he told her, and his smile came straight at her across the car, zooming in like a lightning bolt and holding her in thrall. If the road hadn't been straight she would have crashed right there and then! 'If I thought for one minute that you were an inferior doctor I wouldn't be planning what I'm planning. But...'

'So what are you planning?' It was almost impossible to get her voice to work.

'I'm not free to tell you,' he said softly. 'There's a heap of work to be done before I know whether it's feasible. All in good time, Dr Flemming. For now, trust me.'

'Trust you?'

'Just for two more days,' he told her. 'Just two more days and I'm out of here. For now.'

Good grief! She was so confused she didn't know what to think. Or what to feel. He sat beside her and gazed calmly ahead, and she wanted to throw something at him.

And she knew what she wanted to throw at him. Herself!

CHAPTER EIGHT

It was Ben Hugo was meeting down at the harbour. Ben, the boy who'd saved his life. Christie pulled up beside the dry dock where *Sandpiper* was sitting forlornly, waiting for repair, and Ben rose to meet them. He'd been perched on the rails, staring out over the darkened harbour entrance.

'Ben.' Christie was confused. She cast a look of enquiry at Hugo but he was already greeting the boy.

'How goes it? How's the hand?' He motioned to the dressing on Ben's left hand and Ben grinned.

'It's fine. Dr Flemming stitched me up great. It's starting to itch, though.'

'Itching means it's healing,' Hugo told him. 'So enjoy it and don't scratch.'

'OK.' The kid gave Christie a shy smile and turned to *Sandpiper*. 'Bit of a wreck, isn't she?'

'No bodies aboard, though,' Hugo said softly. 'Thanks to you and your mum.'

The boy flushed crimson under the harbour lights and the look on his face was one of sheer pleasure. Christie could only wonder at the transformation. This was a boy who hadn't been able to bear anyone mentioning his mother for six long years. And now...

'Yeah, she'd be really chuffed,' Ben said, and his eyes glowed. Then he seemed to collect himself, flushed some more—after all, he was still a fourteen-year-old—dug his hands deep in his pockets and tried hard to look like he didn't care. 'Dad said you wanted to see me. I couldn't come before—I had Scouts.'

'This is a good time,' Hugo said easily. He smiled at

137

Christie. 'It means Dr Flemming can hear what I have to say, too. I was wondering if you could help me. You know I'm leaving on Friday?'

Friday, Christie thought. Here it was again. She knew it. Why it hurt so much she didn't know, but she knew it.

'Mmm.' Ben said,

'My dad's staying behind.'

Oh, right. She hadn't known that. Not a one-night stay then.

'Why?' said Ben.

'It's his boat and he loves her,' Hugo told him. 'It's his life. He'll stay in the cottage beside Doc Flemming and he grandpa, and he'll watch over the boat while she's being repaired.'

'So what's that got to do with me?' Ben asked diffidently, and Christie couldn't figure out who was more interested—the boy or her.

'They tell me,' Hugo said slowly, staring out over the windswept harbour, 'that there's been a bit of trouble around here. Vandalism and the like. Boats being tampered with.'

'Really?' Ben opened his eyes wide in innocence and Christie practically boggled. Where did this man get his information? Ben was one troubled kid, and the rumour was that the vandalism was straight down to him.

'I was interested in employing you,' Hugo went on, seemingly unaware of the all-too-innocent gaze. 'I'd be paying, of course, and the job's part time—after school.'

'Doing what?'

'A couple of things,' Hugo told him. 'I want someone to keep an eye on the boat. My dad will be here but he's in his seventies and he can't keep an eye on her at night. I don't mean camp down here or anything. Just keep your eyes and ears open.'

'What else?' Ben was retreating into suspicion mode.

'When my father gets the boat going, will you act as crew?'

Ben stared 'How do you mean?'

'He'll want to test her,' Hugo told him. 'Knowing my dad he'll want to take her out of the harbour. I need someone who's young and strong, who's a bit sensitive to an old man's pride and who knows the sea back to front. Do you reckon you could do that?'

'Not in school hours,' Ben said, and Hugo nodded.

'Dad wouldn't expect that. Also…'

'There's more?

'How are you at lawn-mowing?'

Ben grinned. 'I knew there'd be a catch.'

'Once a week,' Hugo continued inexorably. 'Two cottages. Dad's and the doctors'.'

'What, mine?' Christie frowned. 'Hey, what are we talking about here? I can mow my own grass, thank you very much.'

'When did you last do it?' Hugo demanded, and watched and grinned as she glowered.

'It's healthier if it's left long.'

'Yeah, right.' He turned back to Ben. 'Will you do that, Ben?' And he offered an amount of money that made both Ben and Christie stare.

'What?' Ben couldn't believe he'd heard correctly. 'No island kid earns that much.'

'It's a big responsibility I'm asking you to shoulder,' Hugo told him. 'My father's life, really. And you've already saved mine. Will you take it on?'

'Of course I will.'

'Good man.' Hugo shook Ben's uninjured hand and smiled. 'Great.'

'—I'll be able to save for a sailboard now,' Ben stammered. 'Before…' He hesitated and then decided to make a clean breast of it. 'I've watched the other kids and thought no. But now…' His shoulders came back and he practically strutted. 'I gotta job. You wait till I tell my old man.' And he gave a whoop of pure, unadulterated joy and streaked off homewards.

'So you've just tied another lot of loose ends.' For the life of her Christie couldn't keep her voice from sounding cross. This man was pipping her at every post. 'You know he's been so…angry. He's gone from one spot of trouble to another, almost begging to be caught. Now, in one swoop—'

'You think I might have saved myself a spot of vandalism?'

'I think you might have saved Ben,' she said frankly. 'You've relieved his guilt, you've given him a job and you've trusted him. He's a hero, and now he'll have a little spare cash, too. For a kid with self-esteem somewhere around his socks, you've done a fantastic job.'

'It may not last.'

'But it may.' Christie turned from looking at the damaged boat and her eyes were warm. 'Thank you, Hugo.'

'It's my pleasure.' His eyes were watchful in the dim light. For a moment it had seemed almost natural that he would take her in his arms—or she take him—but he made no move. With difficulty she hauled herself back from her emotional precipice.

'Hugo…' There was something else she needed to say— if only she could concentrate on more than how close his body was.

'Mmm?' He still sounded distant.

'You're not paying to have my lawn done.'

'Ah.' He nodded sagely. 'I wondered when we'd get to that. That's my next point of discussion.'

'Discuss away,' she told him crossly, right off balance, 'but it isn't going to happen.'

'Not even if it's for payment for what you do for my father?'

That set her back. She rocked back on her heels and stared.

'Explain.'

'My father has a bad heart.'

She thought that through and decided he'd told her that already. But what it had to do with her… 'What sort of bad heart?'

'Ischaemic heart disease, but not too bad. He has chronic angina but it doesn't seem to be getting worse. He had a minor heart attack three years ago and had bypass surgery.'

'Results?'

'Excellent,' he told her. 'Apart from a black hole after my mother died, he's been taking much better care of himself. He has his cholesterol down to just under six from over eight so we're going well! His blood pressure's almost normal, he's active again and energetic, and there's no reason to think he won't make it to ninety.'

'I see.' She frowned. 'So why do you want me to look after him?'

'I won't be here,' he said softly.

It had come at last. She bit her lip, but it had to be discussed some time. His leaving. 'You'll leave your dad here for a week or so and then return to sail the boat south with him?'

'No.'

'No?'

'I'm needed urgently,' he told her. 'And I'm afraid I can't come back soon. I moved heaven and earth to get this week off, so as soon as Dad is settled I'm leaving. I need to be in New York on Monday, and back in Brisbane next Friday. I have a locum anaesthetist covering for me but there are limits.'

'Of course.' For the life of her Christie couldn't stop her

voice sounding dull. She frowned. It still didn't make sense. 'Is your father happy to stay here? I mean, I assume it *is* only for a week or so.'

'Alf tells me the boat could take three months. He's working on his own and it's a craftsman's job. I've told him there's no hurry.'

'Three months!' She took a deep breath. *Three months...*

'So what you're doing,' she said softly, her anger building as the ramifications sank home, 'is dumping your dad. More. You've arranged for me to have an elderly man as a neighbour—a man with known heart disease and who has no friends and relatives on the island.'

'I—'

'You don't think you might be adding to my problems?' She was angry now, and it showed. Angry on her own behalf and angry also on the old man's. 'Don't you have time for him in Brisbane? No, of course not. You're obviously a very important specialist. So you'll dump him here and ease your conscience by telling yourself he'll be living next to a doctor.'

'I'm not dumping him.' Good grief, he was putting on his wounded act. Labrador puppy being kicked by the nasty doctor... 'He *wants* to come.'

'Why?'

'He wants to supervise his boat being fixed. He'll enjoy it, and when I suggested it he couldn't agree fast enough. He's bored in Brisbane. I think he and your grandfather will get on like a house on fire, and I suspect it'll be great for both of them.'

But not for me, Christie thought as she fell silent. She couldn't say the words—they were just too mean to utter—but she thought them anyway. As well as all her hospital work and her five hundred islanders, she'd have two old men to look after instead of one. Two to check up on. Two to cook for...

'He's independent,' Hugo told her, as if reading her thoughts, and her eyes flashed.

'*Independent*. How can he be independent if he's in his seventies and knows absolutely no one? How can he be? Though the way you're talking he'll be less alone here than he is in Brisbane. Where's your brother, did you say? In the Bahamas? And you'll be in New York, presenting some very important paper at a very important conference, I'll bet, so you can end up as Professor Tallent—while back here I pick up the pieces of your responsibilities. Good old Christie. She'll do it!'

He didn't say a word. He stood still in the darkness, looking down at her with an expression that was unreadable.

And Christie? She was so angry she was shaking, and she didn't truly understand why. This was just one lonely old man they were talking about and, heaven knew, she had enough lonely old men on her island. One more would make little difference, she knew.

Hugo must go. She'd known he would. So why…?

'Christie…' He seemed unsure of himself, she thought. Conscience, maybe?

Good. He deserved it. Toad!

'I need to go home,' she said bitterly into the wind. 'Now.'

'Christie, wait.' He put a hand on her arm but she wrenched it away.

'Leave it, Hugo. You've got your way. Of course I'll look after your father. You know that. When have I not done everything that was expected of me on this damned island?' She gave herself an angry mental shake and made her voice soften. 'Oh, of course I will, and you don't need to pay by organising my lawns to be mowed either.'

'It's the least I can do,' he said softly. 'And if my plans work out—'

'Don't tell me. You'll up-end your father and re-root him in Manhattan while you take the chair of anaesthetics at America's top university. Or something similar.' She took a deep breath. 'And I'll be still here, wishing you well. But for tonight… Let it be, Hugo. I need to go to bed.'

'With me?'

He said it so simply that for a moment she thought she must have misheard. Her breath snagged in her throat, and her heart skipped a beat. Or six.

'What?'

'No!' He'd caught himself and he looked as startled as she had—as if the words had slipped out, unintended. He gave a rueful smile that had as much weariness in it as hers. 'I'm sorry. It's too soon. Too…crazy. Let me sort myself out, Christie Flemming, and then we'll see where things go. But for tonight… You're right. We need to go to bed. Alone!'

She didn't sleep. How could she? All night Christie tossed and turned, and at dawn she rose feeling like she hadn't been to bed at all.

Needs must. Wednesday was her busiest day of the week, the day she spent on the other side of the island at the Koori settlement. It was a mere few miles but it might as well have been in a different country. The Kooris kept themselves to themselves in quiet dignity, but they represented almost half her patient population. Because they couldn't—or wouldn't—travel, she only had one day a week to devote to them.

So it was Wednesday, she thought drearily as she got out of bed. Wednesday, here goes.

But—apparently—she wouldn't be doing it alone.

Hugo was waiting for her. He rose as she entered the silent kitchen and she almost jumped a foot at the sight of him.

'H-Hugo.'

'I'm not a ghost,' he told her with a weary smile. 'Though I feel ghost-like. Did you get as much sleep as me?'

'I have no idea how much sleep you had,' she said crossly, and he grinned.

'Yep. By the sound of your voice and your lovely sunny temper, I can see you had the same. That's what happens when we sleep one room apart. I lay in the dark and wondered if I could hear your heartbeat.'

Which pretty much summed up what she'd been doing through the night, she thought, but she'd die rather than admit it. This man was a serious flirt.

Two more days and he'd be gone, she told herself. Two more sleeps… Two more nights of listening for heartbeats…

She had to go—now!

'Toast?' he said, and pulled open the fire door. 'I'm getting really good at this.'

'I'm fine,' Christie said shortly. 'I don't need breakfast.'

'Yes, we do,' he told her. 'Ray tells me we have a huge day ahead of us. I'm having breakfast if you're not, so you might as well eat while you wait.'

'We?' She stared. *We?*

'Don't you want me to come with you?' Hugo demanded, loading his toasting fork.

'No. Yes. There's no room in the truck,' she said desperately. 'Mary-anne—'

'Mary-anne's not coming. I talked to her yesterday and asked if I could take her place. She's promised to keep an eye out for your grandpa, like Louise normally does on Wednesdays, and Louise is taking the day off. So, there you have it. Instead of a nurse, today you have me. I can stick on a bandage and load a syringe with the best of them, so if it's OK with you, Doctor…'

'Does what's OK with me have the least bearing on what you intend to do?' she snapped, and he turned from his toasting fork and smiled. It was the smile she was starting to dread.

It started off as the slightest creasing of his eyes and then the brown depths grew warmer and warmer and his eyes locked onto hers—and it was like making love all by itself. It took her breath away and more. It stranded her like a fish out of water but, unfishlike, she felt like she was drowning.

'You have no idea,' he said softly, his smile holding and locking her to him. 'You have no idea, Christie Flemming, just how you're affecting what I intend to do. And I'm dead scared to tell you, because I might be wishing for the moon!'

They drove to the settlement in silence. Christie could think of nothing to say—she couldn't even begin to think of what he'd meant by his enigmatic comments and, bluntly, she was afraid to try.

Hugo, on the other hand, seemed content to sit in silence, and he let his thoughts wander where they willed. He watched the landscape unfold around him. In the dawn light the island was indeed beautiful. As they left the township, the land grew progressively more and more rugged, and the tropical foliage more and more untamed.

This island must once have been under water, he thought. There were inland cliffs, vast ridges of rock reaching for the sky, and the palm-lined track they were on was littered with ancient shells. It was interesting to think about—to force his mind from the girl beside him…

He couldn't let himself think along these lines just yet!

Finally they reached the northernmost tip of the island. Christie pulled to a halt in front of a jagged rockface and turned to her passenger. The silence was finally broken.

'Here we are. House call number one. Coming?'

'House call…' He looked around in amazement for something that could possibly be a house. Nothing!

'Mabs Wasjarra lives here,' Christie said simply, climbing out and retrieving her bag. 'She has cancer—bone metastasis—and she's bedridden.'

'There's no house,' Hugo said cautiously, and Christie smiled.

'Depends what you call a house. Are you coming or not? You'll need your stick.'

He was very glad of his stick. Christie left the car and headed straight for the rockface. Hugo was left to follow as he wished.

He wished. He wasn't being left behind for quids, but by the time he'd climbed the jagged rocks where Christie led, his leg was aching and he was short of breath from the effort.

'This one's our hardest house call,' she said, taking pity on him. 'Mabs refuses to leave. Up here, she can see the world.'

She could at that. From where he stood, Hugo could see the entire island. Far away in the distance the township was waking. Tiny plumes of smoke were wisping from chimneys of far away cottages, and he could see a couple of boats moving from their moorings in the harbour.

The wind was still keening around the island. It was still too rough for boats to face the open sea but the wind was dying, and tomorrow the fishing fleet would be out again. Today they looked as if they were revving their engines in readiness.

Not here. There wasn't an engine in earshot. There was nothing at all! But Christie was stooping, crouching beneath a ledge and motioning him to follow.

'Mabs?' she called. 'It's Doc Christie. Can I come in? I've brought another doctor with me—a man. Do you mind if he comes in, too?'

It was a cave, Hugo thought with incredulity as Christie disappeared under solid rock. The old lady lived in a cave! He stood, stunned, until he heard Christie's voice echoing out from within.

'Mabs says you're very welcome,' Christie called as he stared in amazement at the crevice into which she'd disappeared. 'Come on in, Hugo, but watch your head.'

Watch his head! He had to watch more than that. He had to get down and crawl, which did his bad knee no good at all.

He hardly noticed the discomfort. The whole scenario had him fascinated. This was like no house call he'd ever done.

Once in, it took several minutes to adjust his sight to the gloom. The cave opened up—thankfully—to a chamber as big as a small room. And as high. Here he could stand, and if he was careful he could do it without hitting his head.

The only light was from the entrance but, once the eyes were accustomed, it was enough. The old lady was in a makeshift bed in the corner of the cave. She was an ancient Koori woman, withered and tiny, and Christie was already stooping over her and taking her hand.

'Mabs, this is Dr Tallent,' she said, gesturing back at Hugo. 'He's from Brisbane.'

'He's the fella that darn near drowned,' Mabs whispered in a frail thread of a voice, looking him over from head to toe. 'I hear the spirits nearly got him.'

'They did at that,' Hugo agreed. 'If it hadn't been for one very brave lad, they would have.'

'Eh. Young Ben. I heard. He's a good kid. Comes up here sometimes, but never causes trouble like he does in town. Worries and worries about his ma. I hear you've fixed that a bit, too.'

She winced and moved painfully in her bed, which, now Hugo's eyes had adjusted to the gloom, he saw was a vast mound of furs. 'You oughtn't be afraid of the spirits, though, young fella,' she told him. 'They're coming for me soon enough and I'm not afraid. It's my time, I guess. Eh, Christie?'

Christie smiled. 'Not for a bit yet.'

'More's the pity.' Mabs winced again. Christie asked her a question with her eyes and then lifted the furs away from her body. Mabs was naked beneath, her body creased and leathery, almost parchment-like.

'You've taken the dressings from the ulcers,' Christie said softly, looking down at her legs. 'You promised me you'd leave them on.'

'Didn't feel right,' Mabs told her. 'Damn things hurt.'

'They won't heal if you don't look after them. I asked Cara to change the dressings every day and I left her what she needed to do it. Didn't she do that?'

'She wanted to.' Mabs snorted. 'Did it once and I thought she'd puke. Told her not to do it again.'

'Cara is Mabs's daughter,' Christie explained to Hugo. She sighed. 'Will you let Dr Tallent take a look?'

'He can have all the looks he wants.'

'Will you roll over for me?' Christie asked her gently as Hugo squatted beside her. 'Let me help you. I want Dr Tallent to see your hip.'

And he saw. Good grief! Any Brisbane patient would have been in an acute hospital with these ulcers, Hugo thought grimly. She had massive ulcers on her legs, and the pressure points on her hips were fast turning to bed-sores.

They must be hurting so badly! And Christie said she had bone metastasis to boot. Bone cancer meant pain! He gazed down at the withered, stoic face and could only wonder at the calmness that looked back at him.

'I'm falling to bits,' she said cheerfully enough. 'Told you.'

'Are you alone?'

'Who, me?' She cackled with laughter. 'As alone as I want to be. Why do you think I'm up here? I wanted to be away from them. But, no, I'm not alone. They're here all the time. If it's not one daughter, it's another, or any one of my grandkids. Twenty grandkids I have last time I counted. I lived down there with them on the estuary but when me legs got bad the sand troubled them. Got into the sores and made 'em worse. The pain was real bad so I came up here into the rocks to die.'

She shrugged. 'And it's a grand place. Christie here gives me tablets that make the pain bearable and I haul meself out on the ledge when the sun comes up. I can just look and look. It's all I want to do now.'

'And your family bring you food?' Hugo asked, looking around in wonderment. The cave was clean and smelt sweet enough. Obviously whatever sanitary arrangements she made were working well. There was a fireplace by the entrance, with a couple of pots at the ready. The fire was a heap of glowing embers, there was a pile of firewood and a full billy lay nearby, ready to boil. She was being looked after.

'The kids do a real good job,' Mabs told him. Christie had started attending to the worst of the ulcers, carefully cleaning the edges. It must be hurting, but she didn't flinch. 'I'm lucky.'

Lucky! Hugo looked down at her face and he saw that she meant exactly what she was saying. She was in one of the roughest places in the world, suffering from an incurable disease. She had nothing but her campfire and her skins and a roof over her head, and she thought herself lucky!

He thought of some of his patients back in Brisbane—people who thought they were hard done by because they couldn't afford the latest model Mercedes—and his face twisted into a rueful smile.

But those legs... 'Will you come into hospital for a bit?' he asked her. He stooped and held her leg to examine one of the ulcers gently. It was deep and nasty—any worse and she risked losing the leg. But maybe the cancer was threatening that anyway. He glanced up at Christie and she gave an imperceptible shake of her head. No use trying, her look said.

And Mabs told him just that. She snorted. 'Hospital? Huh!'

'She won't come,' Christie told him. 'You think I haven't tried?'

'We did it once,' Mabs told him. 'Came to what you lot call civilisation. We lived on the outskirts of the city, and we saw what it did to the kids. So we upped and brought everyone here. Now we keep to ourselves, thank you very much. I'll die here with my people, and if I have to die a month or so sooner because of it then that's the way I want it.'

'And that's the way it'll be,' Christie said softly. She was placing ointment on the largest ulcer and wrapping it. 'But the dressing stays on, Mabs. I'm sending Mary-anne out tomorrow and she'll check you every day this week. She'll ask Cara to help, and by the end of the week Cara won't even flinch.'

'I don't need—'

'*I* need,' Christie told her. 'If you don't wear the dressings, I'll feel bad as a doctor. Let me do this for you, Mabs. Let me hold the spirits at bay for a short while longer. So you can lie in the sun and look all you like. Please?'

The old lady looked at her for a long moment, and Christie gazed calmly back. Strength meeting strength. It went on and on, and neither flinched.

And finally the old lady conceded. She gave a hint of a smile and sighed.

'You're a good girl—for a white.'

'And you're a tough old lady—for a black.' Christie grinned down at her, knowing she'd won. 'You'll do it?'

'Yes, all right.' She sighed. 'I guess I wouldn't mind the sun on my face a while longer. Tell Cara I said it's OK.'

'I'll do that.' Christie gave a brief, enquiring glance at Hugo. He nodded and then together they worked on each of the ulcers.

It was very different work—amazingly different from the work Hugo was accustomed to. They worked by the light of a lantern Christie set up beside them but, even so, it was a makeshift job. The woman needed skin grafts, not bandages. She needed morphine infusion and constant turning—maybe even a dose of radiation therapy would help. But they could only do what she permitted.

Finished, finally, Christie rose and packed her bag. As she did, there was a scrabbling sound from the rocks below and a small face appeared in the doorway. A child of about nine or ten greeted them with a cheeky grin and held up a billycan.

'Ma says here's breakfast. She's coming later but it's fish, Gran. Ma says it's best cooked straight away so I'm gonna cook it for you now. Dad speared it this morning and I nearly got one, too.'

'Oh, well done.' Christie smiled her welcome and moved aside so the boy could come in. As he passed she took his chin in her palm and turned him to face her. 'And then come back to the huts, Davey. I want to put antibiotic in those eyes. You've been rubbing them again.'

'Aw, Doc…'

'You want to be blind like Uncle Arrantha?'

'Nah, but—'

'Then come. That's an order.' She smiled her farewell.
'Ready, Hugo?'

But he wasn't quite. He stood, looking down at the lady
on the skins. Those abscesses were never going to heal the
way she was lying. The pressure sores would be getting
worse by the minute, and he could only imagine the pain
from the bone cancer. She needed a mattress.

A mattress wouldn't work here, though. If it rained, the
water would creep in. Skins would dry, or could be
changed, but a mattress would soak up the water and would
be foul in a week.

'What about an airbed?' he asked suddenly.

'An airbed?' Christie paused.

'Mmm. I think it might work well.' He stooped again in
front of Mabs. 'Mabs, you can't tell me those sores don't
hurt, even with Christie's tablets. You're sleeping on furs
but the furs are on hard rock. What if we found you a
mattress that's full of air? You could pile your furs on top
and it'd keep the pressure off the sores.'

'I don't need—'

'You don't need anything,' he told her, 'but you'd be
much, much more comfortable and it would give me real
pleasure to provide it for you.' He hesitated and then took
her hand. 'Mabs, the spirits nearly took me this week,' he
said simply. 'Now they're claiming you. We both know
that. Your time is soon, and you're not afraid, but my gift
to you of an airbed could make your passage so much eas-
ier.'

Christie held her breath. Mabs had refused so much…
For a long, long moment Mabs looked up at him, gazing
at him with eyes that seemed to see so much more. And
then she sighed and her tired eyes creased into a smile.

'Well said, young man,' she said softly. 'You'd fit in
with my people. I accept your gift, and may it be returned
threefold.'

CHAPTER NINE

'How on earth did you manage to get her to agree to d₋
that? If you knew the arguments we've had…'

'Masculine charm,' Hugo said, and grinned, and Christi₋
couldn't suppress a grin back.

'Very convenient. Where do I buy some?'

'You have your own style,' he told her, his smile slip₋
ping. 'Believe me, Christie, you don't need one more ounc₋
of charm than you have right now.'

And that was enough to shut her up all the way to th₋
settlement.

It wasn't far. Just around the next ridge Christie pulle₋
over again, but this time there were signs that people live₋
there.

The settlement was built on the shores of an estuary, ₋
vast expanse of tidal flats. There were coconut palms an₋
tropical foliage, but enough had been cleared for a grou₋
of rough-built huts to be erected on the water's edge.

Each hut was a wooden one-roomer, with an iron roo₋
and a verandah as large as the hut itself. The huts wer₋
clustered around a central area which contained half ₋
dozen campfires, a couple of swings for the kids, a fe₋
tables with logs for seats under the shade of the palms an₋
not much else. It was simple, but it looked a real commu₋
nity.

'These people don't originally come from Briman,
Christie told him, watching his face as he took it all in
'The original Briman Islanders were wiped out by an en₋
thusiastic white settler with a few bags of poisoned flour
These people only arrived here five or six years ago.'

'Why?' But he'd half answered the question himself. This place was beautiful.

'A political guilty conscience granted the Kooris land titles to this place,' Christie told him. 'As Mabs told you, these people—this tribe—were living rough on the city outskirts on the mainland, but they were being decimated.'

'By?'

'By unemployment, by lack of dignity, by poverty.' Christie shrugged. 'A combination of everything. Mabs's parents were full-blood aboriginals who lived off the land as they'd lived off it for thousands of years. It was a noble way of living but it didn't work when they were forced to assimilate fast into a white culture.'

'I know that,' Hugo said grimly. 'We see evidence of it all the time in the mainland hospitals.'

'These people decided they'd had enough,' Christie told him, 'so they formed a group to come here, and a condition of coming was to abide by the tribal rules. They forbid alcohol. They've used aboriginal grant money to employ the very best teachers. They intend to gradually assimilate into the community, but they'll do it on their terms.'

'Fair enough,' Hugo said evenly. 'Where do you fit into this?'

'They have their own healers,' she said. 'But they have Western diseases as well as their own, which they're intelligent enough to know I can help them with. I work with their teachers and with their own medical people. I check the kids' eyes—trachoma could be a huge cause of blindness here. I spend one day a week here and it's never enough. So…' She gave him an enquiring smile. 'Are you ready to help?'

'There's nothing I'd like better,' he said.

A week ago, if anyone had told Hugo that he could spend eight hours sitting in the heat and sand and wind, checking one pair of eyes after another—and enjoy every minute—

he'd have told them they were crazy. But that was just what he did.

Christie had decided she had another doctor, and she was going to squeeze every last inch of usefulness from him before he left.

'I have a lot of chronic patients here,' she told him. 'House calls, private problems—and a session with the teacher. But what I try really hard to do is keep all eyes checked. The sand here causes major problems. Almost half the adult population is suffering from some kind of blindness. If you could just sit and check…'

She introduced him to Maree, an aboriginal woman in her mid-twenties. 'Maree is our community nurse.' Christie's eye messages told him she wasn't a nurse in the way the government recognised nurses but she defied him to say a thing. 'If you let her know the kids who need antibiotics, she'll make sure they get them.'

So that's what he did. He sat and chatted to each child— or teenager—as they hove into view. There seemed some system that he couldn't figure, but every time he finished with a child another would appear. He was stunned by how many needed the antibiotic eyedrops.

He also did a rough check of each child and was dismayed by the number of other minor or not so minor things he found. A little boy sat with his head at an odd angle and when pressed said his ear had been hurting for days. And buzzing. Hugo diagnosed an ear infection and he and Maree cleaned it out and set the healing steps in process.

An older boy who'd stood on coral a week previously had red weals running up to his ankle. If it hadn't been tended to today he might well have risked losing the foot!

He saw a teenager who was burning hot to the touch— 'Just a bug, Doc,' the girl said. 'Maree says I have to drink lots.' Hugo examined her and worried.

He found himself treating all manner of complaints, but

hardly any were brought to his attention without probing. He had the impression they'd be content if problems weren't noticed at all, but they accepted his strictures and treatments with cheerful good humour.

They also took his presence with good humour. His fame had gone before him 'The drowning doc,' they called him, and he had to grin and enjoy it.

And Christie…

They simply called her Doc, and it was transparent that she was held in enormous respect. It was probably because she held them in as much respect, he thought as he watched her talk to a group of young children about the importance of looking after their teeth. She'd brought out a carton of toothbrushes, and she and the teacher spent a solemn hour labelling each child's brush.

'Because it's important not to share,' she told them solemnly. 'If Brenda here has a bug in her tummy, even if she's not sick yet, and she shares her toothbrush with Joe, then Joe will get a bug in his tummy as well.'

Hugo found himself smiling as he watched her draw pictures on a chalkboard under the palm trees, showing Bill Bug in Brenda's tummy, Bill heading up to her mouth, leaping onto her toothbrush and then standing on her tongue with his Bug Telescope, seeking a new home.

This was as far a cry as he could possibly get from his state-of-the-art operating theatres in Brisbane, he thought as he watched her, his admiration growing by the minute.

And the questions in his head kept increasing by the minute. Could he?

So many things had to work if it were to be possible.

The last chapter… He had to concentrate on the last chapter.

No, he told himself fiercely, turning back to the girl he was treating. He had to concentrate on Mary Bindi's eyes, and Anna Corragaba's fever, and for now nothing else mattered.

They finished early.

'I can't believe we're done,' Christie told him as they packed up at about five. 'Having another doctor is magic.'

It was. Hugo looked across at the girl beside him and agreed entirely. Christie was liberally covered with dust, she was wearing jeans and T-shirt and big leather boots—'The snakes around here are murder,' she'd told him that morning—and by the look of her footwear he pitied the snakes.

She'd hauled her curls back with a crimson ribbon, she looked about as far from a doctor as he could possibly get, and she was the most desirable doctor he could imagine. City specialists? Give him Dr Flemming any day...

No! There was time enough for that in the future—please, God. He had to get himself sorted out. There were so many complications, and he wasn't about to start something he couldn't finish. That way lay madness. Or cruelty.

'Want to eat dinner on the beach?' Christie asked.

That stunned him. He'd thought she'd be wanting to get back to Stan. It threw him right off balance. Professional detachment until he left—that was what he'd planned.

But it wasn't what Christie had planned. 'Grandpa doesn't expect me until late, and he eats at the hospital kitchen on Wednesdays. My day here often extends after dark. Mary-anne checks eyes and refers other problems to me, but today you've coped with almost everything yourself.'

He had. Including the fever...

'I persuaded Anna Corragaba's parents to let her go to hospital,' he said diffidently, and Christie smiled.

'Maree told me. Well done. She says Anna's been running a fever for three days, but it's half the battle to get

hese people to admit they're sick, and the other half to
persuade them to do something about it. It'll take her parents a while to get her there, though. They'll walk her
across the island.'

'But she's sick!' Hugo was startled. 'Don't they have a
car?'

'No car.'

'Then can we take her ourselves—or send out the ambulance?'

'What ambulance?' Christie grinned and motioned to her
truck. 'That's it. You're looking at it. And as for getting
Anna into it, there's no possibility she'll agree. The tribal
elders have decided they'd rather die than use cars, and
they mean that literally.'

'Why on earth…?' That didn't make sense.

She hesitated, and then shrugged. It was stupid to share
problems which in two days would mean nothing to him,
but maybe—well, maybe he could write it down in his in-
terminable notes.

'If you knew the trouble they were facing with petrol-
sniffing among the kids before they came here,' she said
softly. 'It was dreadful. I don't know whether you noticed,
but a few of the older kids are damaged because of it.'

He'd wondered. There had been the odd slow-speaking,
slow-thinking teenager in his list of patients.

'So they gave up cars?' he queried. 'It seems a huge
price…'

'It's one they're prepared to pay, and if I'm to be allowed
to treat them then I need to respect that.' She smiled. 'As
you seemed to. I didn't see you forcing any medication
down anyone's throat.'

No. It had taken longer—to explain everything, to gently
persuade—but he was left at the end of the day with the
feeling that he'd done OK. There was a warm feeling in
his gut which didn't only stem from the fact that the sand

was hot under his boots and he was standing next to the
woman he was starting to think meant everything to him..

But she was back on track. Back to business. 'Anna
should get to the hospital by midnight,' she said briskly,
hauling her gear into the back of the truck before he could
stop her. 'The men will carry her most of the way and they
move fast. I'll see her then.'

'I suspect there's a rumbling appendix.'

She screwed up her nose. 'Really? Damn. That'll be a
few hours tonight persuading her folks to let her fly to
Townsville. Which they might or might not. Let's hope it
settles.'

'We could operate on her ourselves,' Hugo suggested,
and watched Christie's face.

Her eyes flew to his, widening at the idea, and suddenly
she smiled. The look of strain the mention of the appendix
had caused eased at once.

Which was all he'd hoped to achieve. It was all he could
ever hope to achieve, he thought, and it was becoming more
important by the minute. To take the load from her shoulders.

'That'd be great,' she said. 'Oh, Hugo, you don't know
how great! To watch kids die because they won't be
helped...' She closed her eyes and Hugo wondered how
many times she'd had to do just that in the past. Alone.
But now... She motioned to the beeper on her waist and
she smiled. 'I'll be beeped if I'm needed at the hospital or
when Anna arrives. Meanwhile, I have our dinner in the
back of the truck. Let's find ourselves a beach to eat it on.'

This was different from the last time they'd eaten on the
beach. Things had moved on. They weren't wet from
prawning, they were no longer doctor-patient or victim-
rescuer and the relationship had drastically changed

They'd worked side by side, they'd done a good job—and they were both very carefully not looking into the future.

Hugo because he didn't know what lay there. And Christie because she knew what did.

Bleakness, she thought as she sat silently on the sand and munched the cold quiche the hospital cook had prepared. She hadn't known how bleak until now. Weirdly, Hugo's offer to operate with her on Anna had left her feeling more miserable than ever. It had forced her to be more aware of her shortcomings, and the problems she faced here in the future.

He'd help her this one time, and then he'd be gone, she thought. She'd be left with Briman Island, and her responsibilities, and she'd be on her own.

Hugo watched her face in the gathering dusk. He wanted to say all sorts of things but he wasn't prepared to voice any of them. One word and he was done, he told himself. He wanted her so much, but to hurt her was unthinkable. Better to walk away. Now.

He hardly tasted the food, or the coffee Christie poured. He drank his coffee without thinking, then stopped and stared out over the sea with his mug cooling in his hands. The wind had died almost completely and there was only the steady rhythm of the surf between them. The steady beating of their hearts.

Christie seemed content with silence, too. Mercifully, her phone was silent. The moon was starting to wax again. It was a fine crescent of silvery gold, casting a soft sheen across the water. The beach she'd led him to was completely deserted.

There was only now, he thought bitterly. The moon and the warmth of the sand, and this woman. What if he could never come back?

Dear heaven… Something was going to break!

'We need to go,' he said abruptly, and rose, holding out his hands to her to help her to her feet.

Mistake. Huge, huge mistake. She swung up; he must have pulled harder than he'd intended because her body sort of landed with a thud against his, so they were standing with her breasts pressed against his chest and there was nowhere left to go.

She didn't pull back. Instead, she stood against him, her lovely face raised to his in mute enquiry.

He shouldn't. He mustn't!

How could he not? A man would have to be inhuman. In two days he'd be gone, and heaven only knew when— or if—he could ever return. It depended on so much.

But that was for the future. Tonight was now.

Christie was now. Christie…

He couldn't. He mustn't!

But somehow holding back was impossible.

Because she was in his arms and he was lifting her, holding her and claiming her as his own. As she was! She was a part of him, this woman, and his body intended to claim her, whether his mind willed it or not.

His mouth met hers. His body was melting into hers, as if they were two halves of a whole, torn asunder at some time in the past but now coming together as they were always meant to since the beginning of time.

She was so lovely. She was his!

And then they were falling, slipping down to where Christie had spread the picnic rug. A rug that was no longer intended for a picnic. They didn't part. Not by an inch. Whatever had held them apart had snapped, fragmented and could no longer be restored.

Christie…

Their need for closeness was desperate. His hands searched, slipping beneath her shirt, feeling the softness and the heat of her skin. Feeling the perfection of her body.

And her hands were doing the same, with a fierceness of possession that he hadn't thought possible.

How was it that someone so wonderful could want him? he thought dazedly. How was it that he hadn't found her until now? She'd been on this island for ever, and he hadn't known that he was incomplete without her.

They parted—somehow—just for seconds. He withdrew, as one last stab of reality somehow surfaced. 'Christie, we can't...'

'Try my doctor's bag,' she said, and her voice was a husky whisper, thick with passion. 'Condoms are in the left-hand pocket.'

'For emergencies such as this?' He felt rather than heard her chuckle.

'I distribute them to all my teenagers who can't wait, and I give them a lecture about being sure,' she whispered.

'And...' He forced himself to ask. 'Are *you* sure?'

'As sure as I'll ever be of anything in my life.' She sighed deeply, arched herself against him and then gave him a solid push away. 'Two seconds, Dr Tallent. This is a life-or-death situation. I'll die if you don't make love to me this minute, and I'm holding you entirely responsible for my resuscitation.'

It was the best!

Christie lay in her lover's arms and stared up at the night sky. The stars were appearing now, one by one, as if exulting in what had just happened.

This wasn't her first time. She was twenty-eight years old, and in the years before she'd returned to the island there'd been two serious relationships. Both times they'd talked of marriage, but the island had called and in the end it hadn't broken her heart to walk away.

She'd thought it had been the island. She'd thought she'd had to walk away because of the islanders' needs.

It was no such thing, she decided. She hadn't been meant to be married to either of the men she'd seriously considered in the past. She hadn't felt like this. Not ever!

If she'd met Hugo at medical school or in her training years… If Hugo had taken her to him then, would she have been so firm in her resolve to practise on Briman Island? Could she have said, No, I can't marry you because I'm needed?

The answer would have had to have been the same, she told herself bleakly, as it would be now if he wanted to take things further—but it was so much harder. Because this man made her feel as she had never dreamed she could feel.

He held her in his arms and she felt cherished and tender and wonderful and loved and…totally complete. As if she was where she was always meant to be.

And she knew now definitely what it was. For the first time in her life, Christie Flemming was totally, uncontrollably, wonderfully in love—with a man who could never be a part of her life.

Hugo held her against him as one would hold a dream.

They were stark naked on the soft rug, with only the warm breeze from across the ocean keeping them covered. There was no need of any other cover. Skin against skin, he had all he ever wanted in his life. All he'd never thought to find was right here against his heart.

His Christie.

He'd never dreamed love-making could be like this. It was a pleasurable act, he'd thought, a satisfaction. But this…

It was all of that and more. So much more! It was a meeting of hearts.

And he knew why. This woman was the woman with whom he wanted to share the rest of his life.

So tell her.

No!

He couldn't. She was trapped, he knew. There was no way she could leave her people and, after seeing the work she was doing, he had no right to try to persuade her. She was needed and loved by so many more than him, and this was her place.

And him?

He was city-born and bred, as had been his parents before him. His life was in the city.

So many complications.

No. Just the one, really, and maybe... His heart gave a surge of hope as he felt her stir beside him. Should he tell her? Talk it through? Say it might happen?

And make promises he couldn't keep? Put on pressure that was unbearable?

Maybe he already had, by making love.

It couldn't matter. What was between them was too strong and too precious to be ignored. If this one night was all they had...if it had to be remembered in isolation his whole life long...then so be it.

He turned and took her to him again. His eyes searched hers in the dim light as he loved her, and he saw all he needed to know written in her eyes. More.

She was his Christie.

His love.

For this night—or for ever?

CHAPTER TEN

ANNA arrived at the hospital just after eleven, and Eileen phoned Christie straight away.

'Hi.' They'd left the mobile phone lying beside them and they were expecting the call, but even so Christie had trouble getting her voice to work. She moved within Hugo's encircling arms and the feel of him was making her dizzy.

'Hi, yourself.' Eileen's curiosity echoed down the line. 'Where are you?''

Wouldn't you like to know? Christie thought, and she felt rather than heard the rumble of laughter deep in Hugo's breast. He could hear, too, then.

'About three miles north,' she said ambiguously, and let Eileen make of that what she would. 'Is there a problem?''

'I have Anna Corragaba here with her people.'

'Good.' It was so hard to make herself concentrate, but somehow she did. 'Hugo suspects appendicitis. Set up an IV line. She's dehydrated—she's been vomiting for days and the walk will have done her no good. Nil by mouth.'

'I already told her that,' Hugo whispered into her ear, and at the other end of the line Eileen gasped in shock as she heard. 'She won't have had anything but water since lunchtime.'

'We're coming in now,' Christie broke in, trying hard not to blush. Good grief! Eileen would now be thinking that Hugo was two inches from the receiver, and the news would be all over the island by breakfast. 'Set up Theatre just in case, and call in another nurse. Judy, is it?' The island nurses took turns to be on call for emergency back-up. 'Is Grandpa OK?'

166

'Mary-anne stayed and played cards with him until ten.' There was a pause and Christie could almost hear the smile on the other end of the line. 'She seemed to think you'd be late. I'll get Judy to pop in and check on the way over.'

'That'd be great.'

'If I'm setting up Theatre…I'm assuming Dr Tallent will give the anaesthetic?'

'He's said he will.'

'Now, isn't that lovely.' Eileen sighed and the romantic purr she made on the end of the line had nothing to do with any appendix.

Great. Her surgical skills were rusty enough, but operating with the entire theatre staff watching her for any sign of romantic interest…

She had no choice. By the time they arrived back at the hospital—and they moved fast—Anna was showing increasingly severe signs of rebound. It was definitely her appendix and a nasty one at that.

'Damn,' Christie said as they prepped. 'I'll bet the thing's burst.'

'We should have insisted she come straight over. We should have made her come in the truck.'

'And how do you do that? By brute force?' Christie sighed. 'No. It'll take time for the elders to get over their hatred of cars. One day they'll do it, but I suspect it won't be until their self-esteem has risen to the point where they feel they can cope with problems of petrol-sniffing another way.'

'How—?'

But she was on the edge. 'I don't know,' she snapped. 'For heaven's sake, Hugo, do you think I don't try? There's only so much one woman can do—'

She broke off. This night was getting too much for her. She'd laid her heart on her sleeve, and now it was threatening to fall and shatter into a thousand pieces.

*　　*　　*

The appendix hadn't burst, but it was messy.

One of the island elders, an old lady called Penny, donned mask and gown and came into the theatre with them. 'She needs to be here,' Christie explained simply, and Hugo had the sense not to ask questions. He was stunned enough with the events of this night. He had to force his mind to concentrate on the anaesthetic and not on Christie, and he had no room for anything else. But he was aware...

They couldn't speak as they operated. The old lady watched everything. She watched with eagle eyes as Hugo gave the pre-med and then the general anaesthetic. Her eyes didn't waver as Anna was intubated and Hugo took over her breathing. She seemed to trust him, but she didn't stop watching for a moment.

Christie made a small incision in the right lower quadrant of the abdomen, and the old lady watched that, too, her eyes narrowing as Judy stepped in to swab away the fluids. Christie moved fast. She located the cawcum, sutured around the base of the appendix and tied a purse-string suture after diathermy to the cut ends.

Easy part done.

'There's local inflammation,' she said briefly through her mask. Judy was handing her swab after swab as she searched for every sign of infection. Her emotional turmoil was on the back burner. It had to be. This wound had to be thoroughly cleaned or they'd end up with a nasty case of peritonitis.

Finally, the peritoneal toilet as complete as she could make it, she sent a message to Hugo with her eyes and started to close. The old lady, who'd been standing two feet from the table, finally seemed to relax.

''Twas a messy business,' she said briefly, and Christie nodded.

'Yes. It was a nasty one, Penny, but I think she'll be

fine. Dr Tallent will set up a drip with antibiotics and we'll keep her in hospital for about a week.'

The woman seemed to consider. 'I can stay?'

'Of course you can stay,' Christie said warmly. 'We'll make a bed for you in Anna's room, and anyone who wants to visit can come whenever they like.'

'It's good.' The old lady gave a toothless smile and nodded. 'I'll go and tell her father.' The men, having carried the girl across the island, had refused to come into the hospital but were standing at the entrance, waiting for news.

'If you like—'

'She'll be all right.' The woman put a hand on Anna's forehead briefly, like a blessing, and nodded to Christie. 'She's safe with you.' Then she nodded to Hugo. 'And him, too. He's OK. For a white.'

'And you'll receive no greater compliment than that,' Christie told him as the door closed behind Penny. 'If you knew what this means…'

'What?' Hugo frowned. He was reversing the anaesthetic but he was aware that the tension in Christie's face couldn't be solely attributed to the emotions of the night.

'I've been left alone with one of their children,' Christie said, and her voice was shaken. She looked up at Hugo and her eyes were bright with unshed tears. 'I'm trusted.'

But Hugo wasn't.

Afterwards, with Anna safely settled in the ward and Penny sleeping beside her, they walked back to the cottage. At the door Christie turned, took Hugo's face in her hands and kissed him full on the mouth. Then, before he could react, she withdrew.

'Thank you for tonight, Hugo. I…I know I practically seduced you, but I wanted to very much, and I'll remember it always.'

'Christie—'

'No more,' she said simply. 'It was wonderful but it's over. We both need to walk away. Starting now.'

And that was that. She didn't wait for a reply, but took herself into the cottage, walked into her bedroom and closed the door.

And he couldn't walk after her.

Dear God, not yet...

Life went on—sort of. The next day Hugo's father arrived.

Charles Tallent was an older version of Hugo, straight and tall and strongly built. Where Hugo's hair was jet black, Charles's was white, but it was still thick and wavy, and his eyes were direct and warm like his son's. Seeing him, Christie saw exactly how Hugo would look in thirty or forty years, and for some reason the thought made the ache around her heart grow even stronger.

It grew worse all day.

She'd seen Charles briefly from the hospital window as he'd arrived at the cottage, but she didn't meet him properly until after work. Thursday's surgery was always frantic, she had a nasty laceration to stitch—she almost called Hugo for help, but remembered that as from tomorrow she'd have to cope alone so she might as well start now—and Anna was still ill enough to require a lot of attention.

But Anna would do fine—thanks to Hugo. Christie closed her mind to the thought of what would have happened if Hugo hadn't been here. He had been, and the nightmares were for tomorrow.

Finally, she did a late evening ward round—Hugo hadn't been near the place all day—and came home to find the Tallents, father and son, had settled into the next-door cottage.

Hugo was no longer living with them.

'But his father's a good man,' Stan told her when she questioned him over dinner. 'Hugo's introduced me and I reckon we'll get along famously. Mind, Hugo's said he's bound to feel adrift so I've promised to keep an eye on him.'

That was a change. Christie blinked.

'He'll be here for a month or two,' Stan continued. 'I've told him he doesn't need to organise a car. He can use mine. And he doesn't mind a game of cards. If it gets quiet in there at night then we'll keep ourselves occupied.'

A tiny flicker of light lit in Christie's darkness. Here was another elderly man, lonely and hungry for company, living right next door. Sure, she might have some extra responsibilities but if it could help Stan—

A knock on the door made her jump. She and Stan were in the middle of clearing dishes and she scooted the last into the sink as Stan ushered in father and son.

'Christie, I'd like you to meet my dad,' Hugo said, and smiled at her. His smile hadn't changed a bit—and it stabbed worse than a knife!

She flushed and turned her attention to Charles—and the same intense but wonderful smile twinkled down at her.

Damn, even when Hugo went she wouldn't be able to escape the memory.

'Christie.' Charles took her hand and held it. 'The woman who gave me back my son.'

'I—'

'They tell me he stopped breathing,' he said gently. He turned and looked at Hugo. 'You don't know…' he said, and went on, in a voice that was laced with pain, 'I have two sons and if anything had happened to either of them, I couldn't bear it. Saving his life… I owe you so much.'

'Hey, that's what I'm here for,' she said flippantly, trying to stop the searing ache in her heart. Hugo was watching her with eyes that mirrored her distress—and there wasn't a thing either of them could do about it. What had happened between them was impossible and both of them knew it.

'I'm a doctor,' she managed, trying desperately for light-ness. 'Saving lives is what I'm paid for. That and handing out pink pills! So... Would you like coffee?'

'No.' Hugo was off balance. Curt even. 'Thank you, Christie, but I need to be out of here early and I have things to organise. The plane leaves at six. I just dropped by to introduce Dad and say goodbye.'

'You'll be back, though, won't you, boy?' Stan said, and Hugo shook his head.

'I'm not sure. It depends on the arrangements Dad makes when the boat's ready for sailing south. But that won't be until we're well clear of the stormy weather, and we may well hire a competent crew this time.'

With more of your money, Christie thought, but she didn't say it. She was feeling sick. This man meant so much to her, and he was leaving. Now! After this moment she might never see him again.

The time of light was over.

He was holding out his hand, and now he took her fingers between his. His hand pressed hers and his eyes held hers. She looked up at him mutely, not understanding what was going on.

Or maybe she did.

He *must* feel the same blind attraction she did. He *must* feel the link that had driven her to lie in his arms. Maybe his heart wasn't wholly untouched. How could it be un-touched?

Hugo knew it was hopeless. He knew there was no way love could grow between them because all it would do would be to cause pain.

So it was better to go. To finish it now.

And now meant... Now!

'Goodbye then, Hugo,' Christie whispered, but she couldn't withdraw her hand. For the life of her she couldn't draw away. 'I... We'll take care of your dad.'

He couldn't bear it. He'd meant to walk in and say good-bye and get out of there. But…

'Come outside,' he said, and it was as if the words were driven from him. 'Just for a moment. Christie, please…'

'Go on,' Stan said, watching the pair of them with eyes that saw way too much. 'Go outside and sort things out, the pair of you.'

As if that were possible!

Because, of course, things couldn't be sorted out. Not just like that. Hugo drew her outside, they stood mutely against the front door—and then he kissed her.

Naturally he kissed her. He had to. It was what he wanted to do most in the world.

It was what he wanted to do for the rest of his life.

Or for this one last time, he thought blindly. One last sweet time. He felt himself drowning in that kiss. His own lovely Christie… His love… He wanted it to go on for ever.

But somehow it had to end. Somehow he must find the strength to pull away. To explain the unexplainable.

'Christie…' At last he drew back, holding her at arm's length, and his voice was rough and raw with passion. 'Christie, love, there's something I need to say.'

'You don't…' She could hardly speak. 'Hugo, it's nothing. You don't need…'

'You didn't seduce me,' he told her, his voice a husky whisper. 'What you said of our time on the beach last night. Of our love-making. You made it sound as if it was all your doing, and I don't want…I badly don't want to leave you feeling like that.'

'Like—'

'Christie, I wanted to make love to you more than life itself,' he said softly. 'It was all I wanted in the world. You make me feel like no other woman has ever made me feel. I thought it would be better to walk away and say nothing, but I've suddenly figured it out. If I asked you to marry me... Sweetheart, you couldn't, could you? There are things that would prevent you from coming with me. You can't walk away from your responsibilities—as I can't walk away from mine.'

'N-no,' she whispered. 'I couldn't marry you. But I'm not asking—'

'You're not asking anything,' he said harshly, his hands tightening on her shoulders. 'Dammit, woman, you demand nothing. You give and you give and you give, and I'm not in a position to bestow anything in return. All I've done is take. But I have this one chance...'

Her eyes flew to his. 'I don't understand what you're saying.'

'And I can't tell you.' He groaned. 'It simply isn't fair. But, Christie, love...' He pulled her to him, and his chin settled on her hair as her breasts moulded to him. It was as if he was taking some last comfort from a dearly beloved thing. Something he might never see again.

'Christie, know that you are loved,' he told her thickly. 'Know that I love you with all my heart, and if things don't work out—if I can't return—then know that I'll always be your friend.'

He broke off, and gave a harsh, bitter laugh. 'That's good, isn't it? Your friend. When I want to be so much more. But Christie...' He tilted her chin, forcing her confused eyes to meet his. 'For now, Dad will know where I am. The contact details will be in our cottage. If there's any trouble, contact me. Promise me you'll contact me if you need me. For anything.'

'I...'

'Promise?'

'I promise,' she said, but her voice was dull. Hell! 'If you need me for anything...' What a stupid thing to say. She needed him for *everything*—right now.

But this was her place. This was her home, and it wasn't

his. He had to leave, and she had to stay. Whatever private torment he was in, it had to have nothing to do with her.

He loved her...

Sure, but he had to leave. They lived in separate worlds.

'I love you, Hugo,' she whispered, and she tilted her face to kiss him on the lips. 'I love you, but you need to leave. Whatever you're trying to figure out... don't bother. We both know we belong in separate worlds, that you've really been a temporary loan on borrowed time. There's no answer for us. But...it's been great.'

'It has,' he said heavily. 'Christie...'

'Hush,' she told him, and placed a finger on his lips. 'Hush, now, Hugo. It's time to leave. It was great—but now it's over.'

There was nothing left to say.

And at six the next morning Hugo Tallent boarded the twin-engined Cessna and left the island.

For ever?

'He's not Hugo Tallent.'

'Sorry?'

Mary-anne was beside herself. She came whooping into the ward where Christie was checking Liz's stitches, waving a newspaper as if it were a flag of triumph. 'He's not Hugo Tallent,' she said again, and plonked herself down on the visitor's chair, exhausted. 'I was reading last week's papers over breakfast—they came in on the plane yesterday—and the story of Hugo's capsize and rescue is all over them.'

'I don't understand.' Christie reapplied the dressing and pulled down Liz's nightgown. 'And you might have knocked—*Sister*.'

Mary-anne took the reproof in the manner in which it had been intended. She grinned at Liz. 'Hey, Liz and I used to go swimming in the altogether when we were five years old, and I've had babies myself. There's nothing she's got I ain't seen a million times before. You want to be modest, Liz, or do you want to hear my news?'

'I forgot modesty the first time I was introduced to pap smears,' Liz said sourly. 'And after pregnancy and childbirth, I'm past caring. Bring in your TV cameras—I'm available.' Her grin returned. She had her baby, all was right with her world. 'So tell!'

'You remember that Ellie sent the news of Hugo's accident to the mainland reporters?'

But Christie didn't want to talk about Hugo. 'I'm busy,' she said. 'You tell your news to Liz.'

But Liz's hand came out and grasped hers. 'Don't you dare pretend indifference, Christie Flemming. We know better. Tell us, Mary-anne.'

'Our Hugo's an author,' Mary-anne said breathlessly— and sat back and waited for a reaction.

'An author,' Liz said at last, dubiously. 'You mean, he's not a doctor? How do you reckon he gave me an anaesthetic, then? It sure seemed to work for me.'

'Oh, he's a doctor, all right,' Mary-anne breathed. 'But only part time. In his other life he's Hugo Mainwaring.'

'Mainwaring...' Liz lay back on her pillows and stared at her friend in astonishment. '*The* Hugo Mainwaring?'

'How many Hugo Mainwarings are there?' Mary-anne demanded. 'Look.' She held up the paper and there it was, in black and white. FAMOUS AUTHOR SAVED FROM CERTAIN DEATH! It's him all right.'

'Famous author,' Christie said blankly. She was filling in Liz's chart, but she was working on automatic pilot. 'Like...how famous?'

'Oh, Christie, don't you know anything?'

'Nope,' Christie agreed equably. 'I don't.' The last few years had hardly given her time to keep up with literary matters. It was as much as she could cope with, keeping up with essential medical journals.

'Hugo Mainwaring is only the world's best author of medical thrillers,' Mary-anne breathed. 'They're brilliant. They're full of forensic pathology, medical murders and gruesome details that make your hair curl. And the plots! They're truly brilliant.'

'I love what he does with his research,' Liz added, awed. 'He never gets anything wrong. He writes about things as if he's done them. The simplest experience—everything—comes to life when you read his stuff…'

Like…like operating on a dog, Christie thought blankly. Or catching an octopus by the toe…

'He writes one book a year,' Mary-anne went on. 'He's paid a fortune. His publishers—his readers—want him to write more, but he won't because he loves his medicine. He says he's a doctor first and an author second. But the publicity… It must drive him nuts. Why someone didn't recognise him here?'

But Christie's mind was going in all sorts of directions. His notes. His wide knowledge… So this was the source of the money. This was why he wrote and wrote…

'I've seen him,' Liz was saying. 'In the women's magazines. I've seen him! Why didn't I recognise him? I guess he's been in suits in the publicity photos—not second-hand fisherman's clothes. He goes out with all the models… They say he's one of Australia's most eligible bachelors.'

'Yeah, and that's what he'll stay,' Mary-anne jeered. 'Where does he find the time for a love life with all that on his plate? Heaven help any woman he ever married. Medicine and fame! Now, there's a combination for a good marriage—I don't think!'

But Liz was looking at Christie strangely. 'If a woman loved him, it wouldn't put her off,' she said softly, and her gaze was assessing.

'Oh, yeah, right,' Christie said mockingly. 'Are we talking about me here, Liz Myers? Fat chance. I'll fit in a bit of compact love life on a Thursday afternoon in two months' time when he comes to visit his father—if he comes—shall I?'

'Christie…'

'Leave it, Liz,' she said heavily. 'I knew I was being a fool, and all I know now is that I was an even bigger one than I thought. Hugo Mainwaring…. Well, well. When I fall, I sure know how to fall hard!'

And that was that! After such a confession, her friends didn't broach the subject again. After all, she was right, wasn't she? They couldn't see a happy ending any more clearly than she could. Hugo had left.

All that was left was his memory.

And his father, who the islanders promptly took to their hearts.

It was as if Charles Tallent was one of them, Christie thought wonderingly a month after Hugo had left. He was an intelligent, erudite man of the world, and yet he met the islanders on their own terms, whatever those terms might be.

With Christie's grandfather he discussed the books they'd read, he played chess, he drove down to the harbour and stood on the jetty in the sun and gossiped for hours.

With Alf, the man who was repairing his boat, he showed he understood every step the boat-builder was taking.

He met Ben as a friend, and man and boy got on like a house on fire. Christie would often drive past the harbour and see the pair sitting on the jetty, discussing the state of the world. Ben was a different child to the sulky boy of the past. He was running the local Nippers lifesaving club, he was doing excellently in school and Christie could only wonder at the change. How much was due to Charles? Or…Hugo?

Clued up by Hugo, Charles took a personal interest in Mandy's exam results, and when she achieved the ones she needed to attend vet school it was he who organised the party.

And that was the other amazing thing. The man could cook! The wonderment was still in Christie's head every time she thought about it. Tired and heartsick, the day after Hugo had left, she'd returned to the cottage at night, expecting to cook for two old men, but had found a note which had directed her next door. Ready and waiting, there'd been a chicken pie to die for, followed by raspberry soufflé…

'This is my thanks to you,' Hugo's father had told her. 'As many dinners as you want for however long you want them. For saving my son.'

'He's cooked all over the world,' Stan had told her gleefully. 'In the best restaurants…'

'It's never made me a million, like my son's writing,' Charles had said ruefully. 'But I love it.'

'So…' There were so many things she didn't understand. 'Why did you end up in Brisbane?'

'My wife and I had to settle on one place for the boy's schooling,' he told her. 'My wife loved Brisbane, and it was great for her arthritis. It's not Paris as far as the restaurant scene goes, but it was good enough for us. And then…' His face grew grave. 'Our Peter got himself into one financial scrape after another and somehow there was never enough money to think of moving on. Once my wife died…'

He shrugged. 'Well, the boys are my life. But now Peter's gone and Hugo's busy…' He smiled and shrugged again. 'Enough. For now I have two friends to feed, and who could ask for more?'

Hugo telephoned from time to time, Charles told them, and he was always lit up after such a call. But more and more he didn't wait for the calls. More and more he assimilated into island life.

So it was a happy-ever-after scenario for everyone, Christie thought drearily as one month stretched to two. Even Gloria seemed content. To her amazement, Christie saw her on the beach one night—*throwing balls for Scrubbit!* She couldn't believe her eyes.

Happy ever after was everywhere, she thought bleakly. Happy ever after was for everyone, except her.

CHAPTER ELEVEN

MABS WASJARRA died late on a Friday night, almost three months after Hugo had left.

Christie had sat with her all day. At the end Mabs's pain levels had risen. She'd needed a constant infusion of morphine and she'd loathed the thought of dying in hospital, so for those last few days Christie and Mary-anne and Glenys had taken it in turns to keep watch. At the end it had to be Christie. She had been adjusting Mabs's medication every hour or so, enabling the old lady to stay wakeful and pain-free until the end.

And finally she died, at peace, with her people around her, and if there were tears on Christie's face as she emerged from the old lady's cave for the last time, well, who could blame her? They weren't tears of grief for the old lady whose time it had been to die. They were tears for something else far, far deeper.

It was dusk. Christie stood and stretched her stiff limbs as she looked out over the island, and a sense of desolation welled up within her to such an extent that it threatened to overwhelm her.

Why? This was destiny, she thought bleakly. An old lady's destiny.

As hers was. She, like Mabs, had made the decision to stay with her people.

She closed her eyes for a long, long moment.

When she opened them Hugo was there.

He must have been there all the time, she thought blankly. He'd risen from where he'd been sitting on a rocky

181

ledge to the side of the cave entrance. He'd been watching for her. For…for how long?

Christie could only stare as he came towards her, and she was so stunned she couldn't move.

'It's over?' he asked softly, and she nodded.

'Yes.' There seemed nothing else to say.

'Dad told me where you were—and what was happening.' He gestured inside the cave. A soft keening was coming from within as the Koori daughters bade their mother farewell. 'She died peacefully?'

'She did.' Christie tilted her chin. 'Yes.'

'I'm glad.' He turned and gazed out over the island where the sun was setting over the horizon. 'I can't think of a place I'd rather die.'

'It is lovely.'

Silence.

Then, into the silence, as if it was the most natural thing in the world—as if it was an extension of what he'd just said—he said simply, 'Christie, maybe it's fate that I came back this day,' he said simply. 'It feels like it. Life and death… It seems so right.'

And then he turned to her and took her hands in his. 'Christie, love, this is where I want to live out my life. It's also the place where I want to have my children. Christie, will you marry me?'

It quite simply took her breath away.

'What?'

As an answer to a proposal it was less than perfect, but for a long moment she thought she must have misheard. But Hugo was gazing down at her and there was such a look of longing in his eyes that she knew, right there and then, that she hadn't misheard a thing.

Her Hugo…

He was dressed as he'd travelled, she guessed. They didn't match. He was casually dressed, but expensive and neat, while she'd been crouched in a dusty cave all day. Her jeans were torn and her face was streaked with dust. She'd wept a little at the end, and there were tear tracks in the dust on her cheeks.

She must look dreadful—light years away from this man's world.

Still he held her, and his eyes held hers and the look in them said that she wasn't mistaken at all. However she looked…

But nothing had changed. Nothing! How could he be standing here and asking her to marry him?

'I'm not asking you to leave the island,' he told her, guessing her thoughts. 'I'd never do that.'

'Hugo—'

'Hear me out.' His grip on her hands tightened as if he was afraid that if he released her she'd vanish into thin air. 'I couldn't say any of this before. I couldn't tell you. It seemed so unfair. But…' He looked deeply into her eyes and he sighed, as if he read some immutable truth there that couldn't be denied. 'You do still love me, don't you?'

'Yes,' she said simply. There was nothing else to say. Here on the ledge on top of the world, with the man she loved with all her heart standing right before her, there was room only for the truth.

His breath came out in a long, long sigh, as if he hadn't been sure up until now. As if by leaving her, he'd risked all. 'And I still love you, Christie,' he told her. 'I love you more than life itself. From the moment I first saw you I loved you, and it's grown stronger every minute. But I didn't know how it could work. I couldn't say…'

'What?' Her voice wasn't making it above a whisper. There was a bubble of joy building within her, and it threatened to burst at any moment. This was like a dream and she might wake. She was almost afraid to breathe. 'Hugo, what?'

'I told you, I have responsibilities as well,' he said. '
can't escape them. My father gave up so much for his fam
ily. Because of my mother's arthritis—and her whims—h
moved to Brisbane. Because of Peter's gambling and othe
troubles, he stayed there. He's paid and paid Peter'
debts—he's a poor man because of them and he could hav
been rich. He could have cooked in the best restaurants in
the world. And now my mother's dead and my brother'
overseas. Heaven knows if he'll ever come home, so al
the family he has is me.'

'But—'

'So I couldn't leave him,' he said simply. 'Even thoug
I met this bewitching, wonderful woman who I wanted t
spend my whole life with, she lived in such an isolate
place that I couldn't move to live with her. My father'
health is okay now, but in the future it won't be. If he ha
a heart attack in Brisbane while I was here, then I couldn'
reach him fast. If there was a storm it could be weeks be
fore I could leave the island.' He shrugged. 'Maybe i
shouldn't have mattered...'

'But it did,' Christie said softly, her heart singing as sh
finally saw. 'Oh, Hugo, of course it did. I can't leave th
island because of my family, and you couldn't stay her
because of yours. I couldn't love you if you were any othe
way. But...' The sense of unreality was deepening by th
minute. 'You...you'd really want to come here?' Her hear
was refusing to beat. The world was standing still on it
axis, threatening to tilt her over the edge. 'To live?'

'It could work,' Hugo told her exultantly. 'It will. Sure
I've enjoyed working as an anaesthetist. I trained hard t
get there, but since my writing career started more an
more I found I didn't want to specialise.'

'And you really are a writer?' She knew that now fo
sure, but she needed to hear him say it. She needed thes
crazy, wonderful jigsaw pieces to come together...

'I really am a writer,' he told her lovingly. 'I wrote my first book for fun, and it's skyrocketed out of control. Even though it's still fun, to be honest, I haven't coped well with the publicity. Maybe I should have confessed all from the start, but it was such a novelty not to be known that at first I let it be. And then, when I fell in love with you... Christie, my writing was all tied up with what I wanted for my future, and part of that future was you. I couldn't talk of what I was—without including you.'

Her world was standing still. She was scarcely daring to breathe and it was as much as she could do to get her voice to work at all. Somehow she must. 'You still want to practise medicine?' she whispered.

'Being a doctor is what I am,' he said simply. 'Writing's great, but I'm a doctor first. I want the diversity of general practice and I hate the buzz of publicity. Here—practising medicine with you—building this hospital up, doing the work you're doing, keeping my writing going... Christie, we could have a great life.'

'We...'

'We,' he said softly. 'You and me. And Dad and your grandfather, too.'

'I'm not sure I understand.' She was so confused she couldn't think straight. 'Why...?'

He sighed. He had to make her see. He must.

'Christie, if I'd asked my father to come and live here he would have agreed—as he's agreed to everything his family has ever asked of him,' he said softly. 'But I couldn't do that. My brother—and to a certain extent my mother as well—used him and used him unmercifully. They took over his life. So I couldn't ask it of him. Instead I guess I took a risk. I suggested he spend some time here while the yacht was being repaired. And then I left and I waited. And I hoped.'

Hugo paused. Her eyes were glistening with unshed

tears. He was gazing down at her with such an expression she'd never thought to see on his face. It was an expression that told her everything she needed to know about this man and more.

'Then last week I rang my father and asked if it was time to bring the boat south,' he said in a voice that was suddenly exultant. 'And he told me that he'd rather stay put, thank you very much. If I could find the time to visit every so often—if I didn't mind—he'd prefer to live here permanently because he'd found the place where he'd like to spend the rest of his life.'

'Oh, Hugo!' She felt as if she'd had all her breath sucked out from her lungs. 'Hugo…'

'As I have,' he said strongly, and his arms came around her and he held her close. 'As I have, Christie, love. So what do you say? Will you marry me? Can you bear to put up with another doctor in the family? And a writer? And a very failed sailor?'

'Hugo…' But the word wasn't just a repetition of his name.

It was a vow.

He held her away from him, and he looked deep into her eyes.

'Marry me, Christie,' he said softly. 'Give me my happy ever-after ending that I've been looking for all my life. Please…'

There was no need for her to answer. She reached up and took his face between her hands, and she kissed him.

For now—and for ever.

Behind them, inside the cave, the old Koori woman's spirit had finally left her, going to her ancestors as generation upon generation of her people had done before her. It had been time for her to die.

As it was time for this young couple to come together. For their life—and for the lives within them—to start.

From this day forward.

MILLS & BOON®

Makes any time special™

Mills & Boon publish 29 new titles every month. Select from...

Modern Romance™   Tender Romance™

Sensual Romance™

Medical Romance™   Historical Romance™

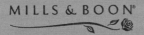

MILLS & BOON®

Medical Romance™

RELUCTANT PARTNERS *by Margaret Barker*

When the man who Dr Jane Crowther believes stood her up all those years ago joins her practice she is determined not to fall for his charms again. But GP Richard has no recollection of their date and sets about trying to unravel the past and to win Jane's love…

THE MIDWIFE'S CHILD *by Sarah Morgan*

Not wanting to force Jed Matthews into marriage midwife Brooke Daniels had fled after their night of passion together six years ago. Now he's back in her life and very interested in getting back in her bed but she has a secret that will change their lives forever…

SARA'S SECRET *by Anne Herries*

When Sister Sara and surgeon Richard Dalton meet there is instant chemistry between them. But with both of them traumatised by experiences in the past how can they ever overcome their fears and find love together?

On sale 6th April 2001

Available at most branches of WH Smith, Tesco, Martins, Borders, Easons, Volume One/James Thin and most good paperback bookshops 0301/03b

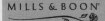

FREE
4 BOOKS
AND A SURPRISE GIFT!

We would like to take this opportunity to thank you for reading this Mills & Boon® book by offering you the chance to take FOUR more specially selected titles from the Medical Romance™ series absolutely FREE! We're also making this offer to introduce you to the benefits of the Reader Service™ —

- ★ FREE home delivery
- ★ FREE monthly Newsletter
- ★ FREE gifts and competitions
- ★ Exclusive Reader Service discounts
- ★ Books available before they're in the shops

Accepting these FREE books and gift places you under no obligation to buy; you may cancel at any time, even after receiving your free shipment. Simply complete your details below and return the entire page to the address below. **You don't even need a stamp!**

YES! Please send me 4 free Medical Romance books and a surprise gift. I understand that unless you hear from me, I will receive 6 superb new titles every month for just £2.49 each, postage and packing free. I am under no obligation to purchase any books and may cancel my subscription at any time. The free books and gift will be mine to keep in any case.

MIZEC

Ms/Mrs/Miss/Mr ....Initials ....
BLOCK CAPITALS PLEASE

Surname ....

Address ....

....

....Postcode ....

Send this whole page to:
UK: FREEPOST CN81, Croydon, CR9 3WZ
EIRE: PO Box 4546, Kilcock, County Kildare (stamp required)

Offer valid in UK and Eire only and not available to current Reader Service subscribers to this series. We reserve the right to refuse an application and applicants must be aged 18 years or over. Only one application per household. Terms and prices subject to change without notice. Offer expires 30th September 2001. As a result of this application, you may receive further offers from Harlequin Mills & Boon Limited and other carefully selected companies. If you would prefer not to share in this opportunity please write to The Data Manager at the address above.

Mills & Boon® is a registered trademark owned by Harlequin Mills & Boon Limited.
Medical Romance™ is being used as a trademark.